SEEN LIKE IT."

INTRODU[CING]
GMC ENV[OY]

For a full product demonstration go to www.gmc.com/envoyxuv

THE ALL-NEW ENVOY XUV, THE ONLY SUV WITH A POWER-SLIDING REAR ROOF. IT ALSO FEATURES A DROP OR SWING TAILGATE AND A FOLDING MIDGATE WITH POWER GLASS THAT SEALS THE PASSENGER SEATING FROM THE ALL-WEATHER CARGO AREA. COMBINED WITH THE POWER AND COMFORT FOUND IN EVERY ENVOY, THE ENVOY XUV IS THE MOST ADAPTABLE SUV EVER. PROFESSIONAL GRADE ENGINEERING. IT'S NOT MORE THAN YOU NEED. JUST MORE THAN YOU'RE USED TO.

WE ARE PROFESSIONAL GRADE™ | **GMC**

 ONSTAR IS AVAILABLE WITH EMERGENCY SERVICES, STOLEN VEHICLE TRACKING, AND REMOTE DOOR UNLOCK.

exploring
SPACE

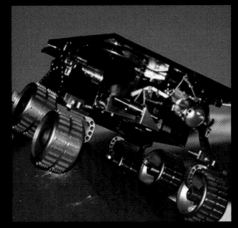

CONTENTS

we have liftoff

the shoreless cosmos

planetary siblings

a world called home

ON OUR WEBSITE

nationalgeographic.com/magazine/space

- **Register to win a telescope.**
- **Order this collector's edition online.**
- **Test your space smarts with our trivia game.**
- **Download out-of-this-world desktop images.**
- **Surprise a friend with an e-greeting.**
- **See animations and video of images in this book.**

Above: Glowing gas streaming from a dying star—
a few times larger than our own sun—resembles the lobes
of an insect's body, giving the Ant Nebula its name.

ON OUR COVER

Saturn's rings were at their maximum tilt of 27° when
the Hubble Space Telescope took this ultraviolet image
on March 7, 2003. Such a view of the planet's rings
and south pole won't happen again until 2032.

Preceding pages: Untethered from the space shuttle,
Bruce McCandless II drifts 217 miles above Earth using
a nitrogen-propelled backpack in February 1984.

A buoyant Neil Armstrong chills out in the Naval Training Tank in Pensacola, Florida, after a simulated water landing. At the time, he was preparing for the flight of Gemini 8, which lifted off on March 16, 1966. Three years later Armstrong became the first human to walk on the moon.

Preceding pages: The Horsehead Nebula rears up against a cosmic curtain of gas 1,500 light-years from Earth. Thick dust makes up the dark region of the horse's head, while ionized hydrogen glows red behind the nebula. The brightest star at left is one of three in Orion's belt.

ABOVE: NASA • PRECEDING PAGES: DAVID MALIN, ANGLO-AUSTRALIAN OBSERVATORY; ROYAL OBSERVATORY EDINBURGH

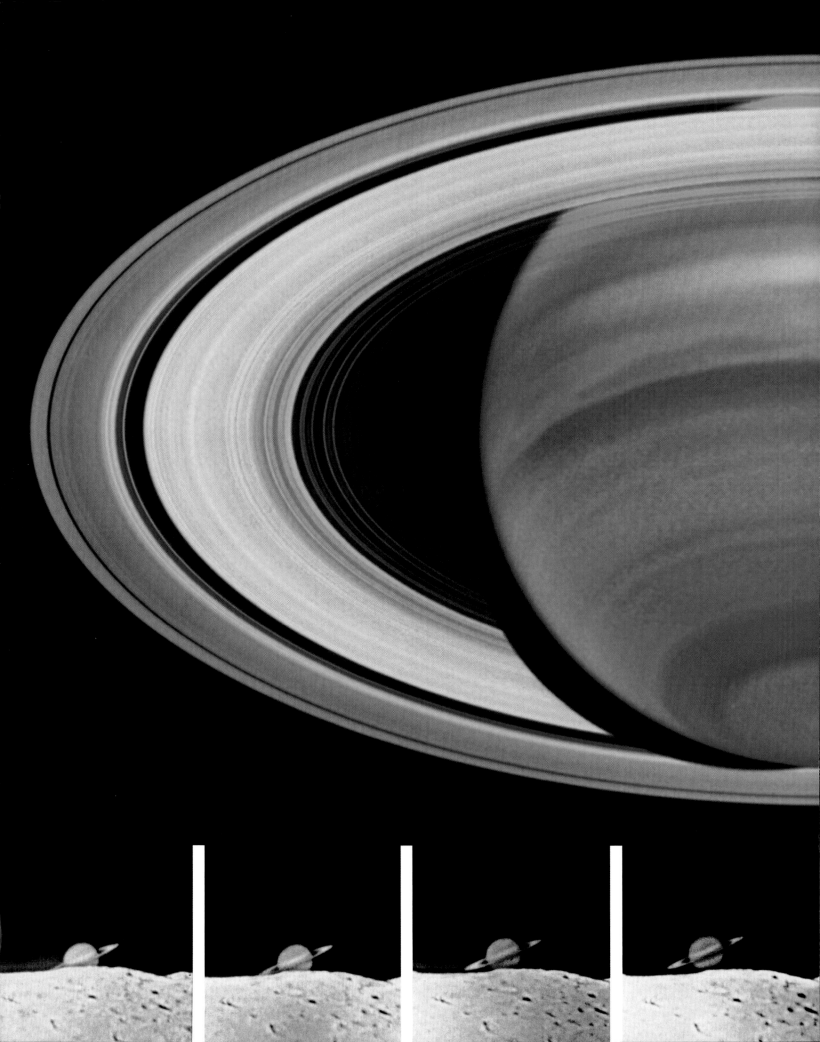

John Young gives a playful salute during the Apollo 16 lunar mission in 1972. A close look reveals that he's bounding a foot and a half off the lunar surface. On Earth, Young in his bulky suit would have tipped the scales at almost 400 pounds, but on the moon he weighed only about 65 pounds.

Preceding pages: Winds as strong as a thousand miles an hour stripe the atmosphere of Saturn in an ultraviolet image captured on March 7, 2003, by the Hubble Space Telescope. The ringed planet appears to be rising above the horizon of Earth's moon in a series of frames taken in 1967 at the New Mexico State University Observatory in Las Cruces.

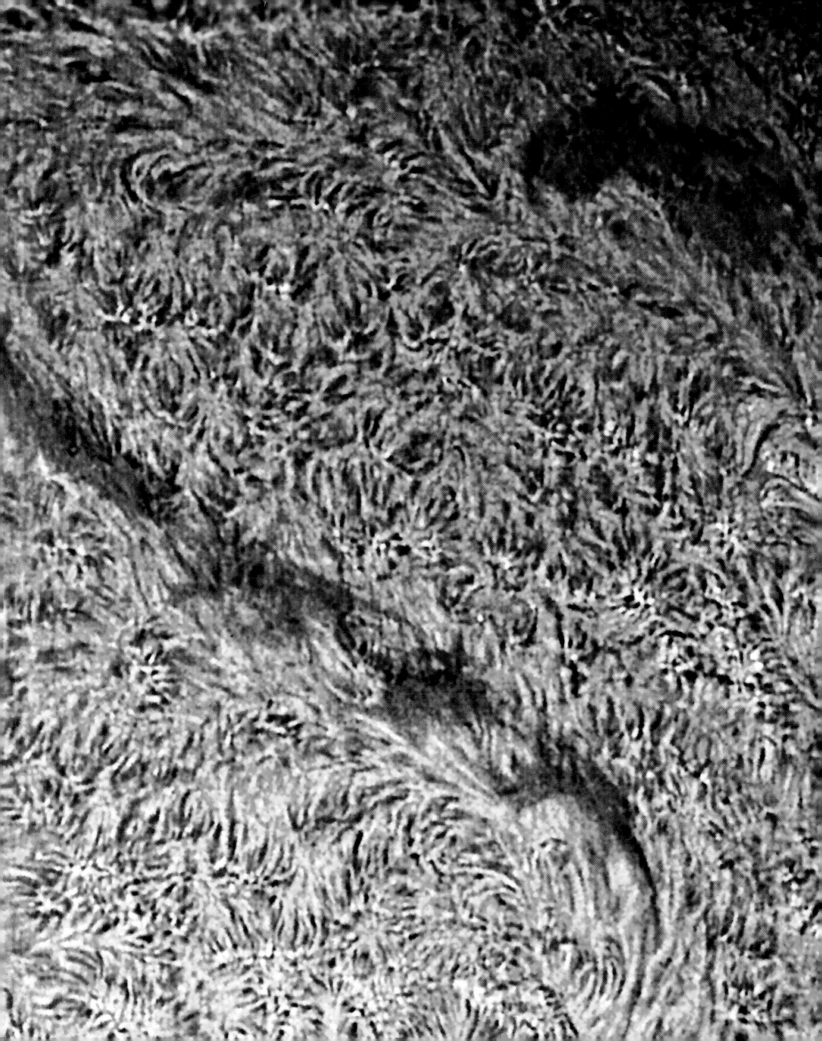

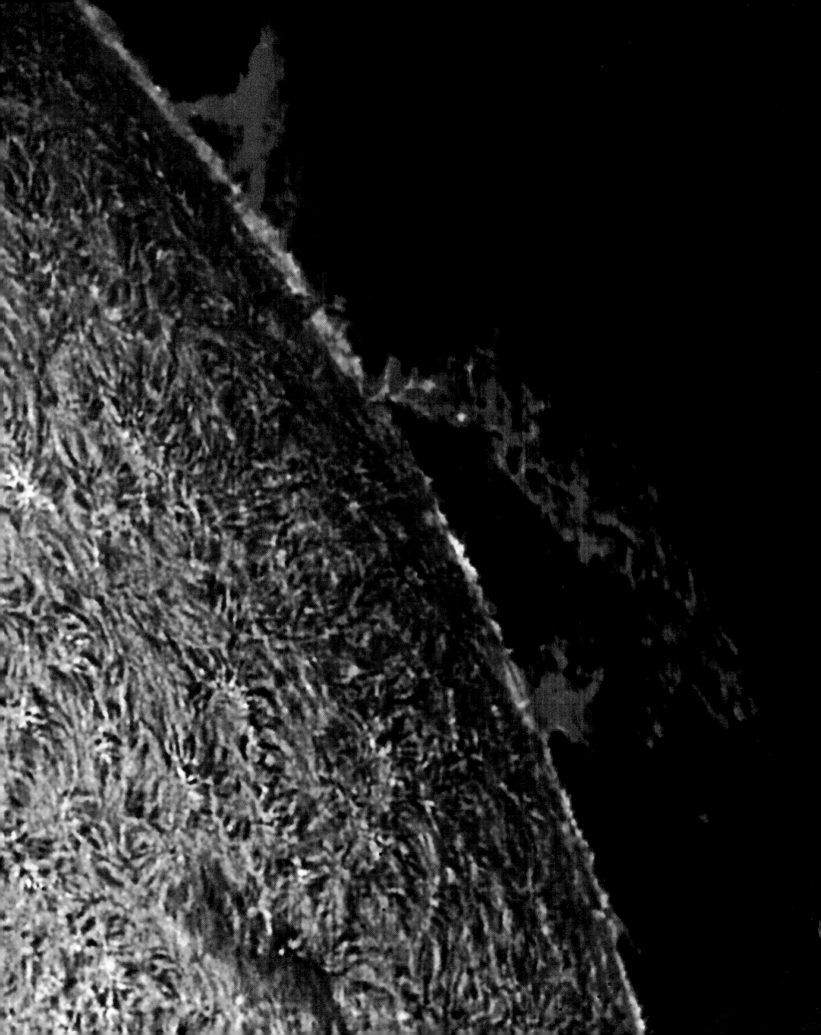

Sharing a once-in-a-lifetime moment, a pair of young stargazers in Pennsylvania watch comet Hale-Bopp light up the sky in April 1997. Named for Alan Hale and Tom Bopp, who spotted it two years earlier when it was just a speck, the comet was one of the brightest ever seen. It will return about 4377.

Preceding pages: Soaring arcs of gas called prominences leap off the sun with the energy of ten million volcanoes. Other large prominences appear silhouetted against the surface.

ABOVE: JERRY LODRIGUSS • PRECEDING PAGES: JACK NEWTON

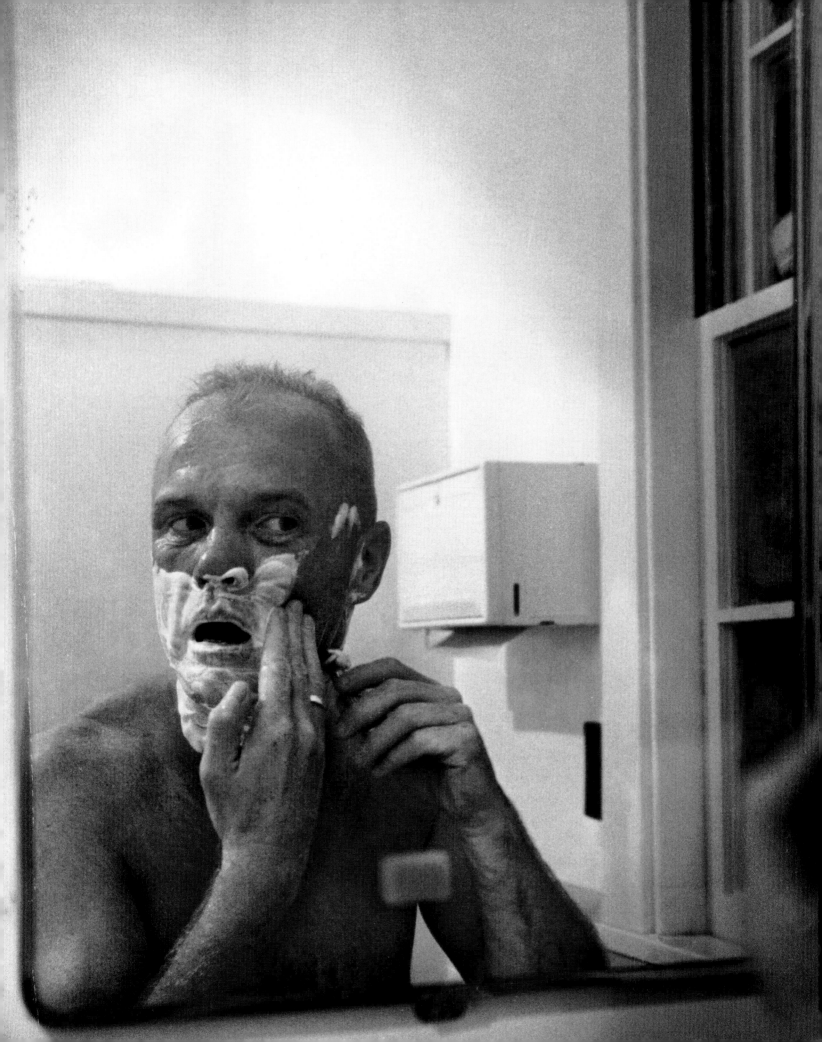

eternal frontier

AFTER 40 YEARS OR SO OF ANSWERING QUESTIONS about my days as an astronaut, I thought I'd heard them all. But NATIONAL GEOGRAPHIC's Editor in Chief Bill Allen caught me by surprise. Pointing to a photograph of me shaving on launch day in 1962, he asked what I was thinking at that moment.

"Well, I suppose I was just concentrating on not cutting myself," I said. "That would have been a lousy start to what I hoped was going to be a great day."

It wasn't the first time I'd gone through the launch preparation routine for the first U.S. manned orbital flight. In fact, it was the 11th. On three previous occasions I'd gotten as far as suiting up, and on two attempts I'd sat for several hours in the *Friendship 7* capsule on the Atlas rocket booster, 80 feet above the launchpad, only to have the mission scrubbed. But this day, February 20, did indeed turn out to be a great one: liftoff at 9:47 a.m., the surge of the rocket, the slow buildup to nearly 8 g's, and then, five minutes into the flight, the first sensation of weightlessness.

What a beautiful sight Earth was! The brilliant blue ocean. Sandstorms across the Sahara. Lightning dancing in the clouds. When sunset came 40 minutes into the flight—the first of four for me that day—it shone with all the colors of the spectrum, from red and orange to indigo and violet.

Three orbits later, reentry was a different story. Controllers had seen a signal indicating a possible problem with the capsule's heat shield, so I was advised to keep the retrorocket pack attached to hold the heat shield in place. To complicate things, the automatic flight controls weren't working, so I was flying the craft manually as I reentered the atmosphere. Looking out the small window, I saw flaming pieces of metal fly by and a bright orange fireball. I couldn't be certain if they were pieces of the already fired retrorockets or *Friendship 7*'s disintegrating heat shield. But the capsule held up fine—the heat shield signal was an error—and roughly five hours after leaving Florida I was bobbing in the Atlantic waiting for a Navy destroyer to pick me up.

A lot changed between that 1962 flight and my second trip into space 36 years later on the shuttle *Discovery* (I'm training for that flight, below). The focus of U.S. space activity had shifted completely from "Can we do it?" to "What can we learn?" There were 83 research projects on *Discovery,* varying from solar observations to a bioreactor useful for cancer studies, to studies of rice seedlings that could lead to greater production, to defining changes in metal alloys melted and cooled in space. At age 77, I was to be a guinea pig for research into changes that occur not only in the elderly here on Earth but also in younger astronauts in space, such as osteoporosis, alterations in the body's immune system, muscle protein replenishment, balance, and cardiovascular effects. Such studies may provide insights into reducing the frailties of old age as well as making longer spaceflights possible.

Some people claim that manned flights are no longer necessary, that unmanned spacecraft can do the job as well. That argument has never made much sense to me. Of course we should use unmanned technology if it can gather information cheaper and with zero human risk. But there comes a time when learning about the new and unknown can only be accomplished by human presence. Space is a most hostile environment. The *Challenger* and *Columbia* accidents were heartrending. But space exploration must continue, not just as a memorial the astronauts would have wanted, but also because of the value of research and discovery. I'm

JOE McNALLY

reminded of a slogan on a Marine Corps fighter squadron bulletin board: "Flying in itself is not inherently dangerous, but it is mercilessly unforgiving of human error." We must reduce that human error.

There are also intangibles to spaceflight. A nation that aspires to be a world leader must be visibly preeminent in science and technology. Statements by Chinese officials after their manned orbital flight in October 2003 revealed that international recognition was a prime objective of their ambitious space program. India and Japan are rumored to have similar aspirations. My hope is that the International Space Station, as a cooperative effort among 16 nations, can serve as a model for the future. Space is the one place we have not yet fought a war. We must keep it that way.

Futile as it may sometimes seem, we can hope for a day when words written by Archibald MacLeish in 1968 will be accepted by all: "To see the earth as it truly is, small and blue and beautiful in that eternal silence where it floats, is to see ourselves as riders on the earth together, brothers on that bright loveliness in the eternal cold—brothers who know now they are truly brothers."

John Glenn

NATIONAL GEOGRAPHIC

EXPLORING SPACE

EDITOR IN CHIEF
William L. Allen

MANAGING EDITOR
Peter Miller

DESIGN EDITOR
David C. Whitmore

ILLUSTRATIONS EDITOR
Kurt F. Mutchler

TEXT EDITOR
Michael Klesius

RESEARCH EDITOR
Barbara W. McConnell

DESIGN AND PRODUCTION
Janel F. Kiley

ILLUSTRATIONS RESEARCH
Bethany Powell

PHOTO RIGHTS
Jean Stringer

SPACE CADETS
Robert L. Booth, David Brindley, Bernard Ohanian, Lesley B. Rogers, Jane Vessels

WRITERS
Diana Ahrens, Vanessa Ampolini, Chris Carroll, Whitney Dangerfield, Scott Elder, Cassandra Franklin-Barbajosa, Beth Goulart, Peter Gwin, Jennifer Steinberg Holland, Andrew Ignacio, Karen E. Lange, Marisa Larson, Cathleen S. Lineberry, Erika Lloyd, Alan Mairson, Miki Meek, Meaghan Mulholland, Katherine Ressler, Naomi Schwarz, Cliff Tarpy, Marie Tutko, Christy Ullrich, Caroline Wallinger, Lynne Warren, Pamela Wells, Sarah White, Carrie Young, Margaret G. Zackowitz

RESEARCHERS
Karen Font, Nora Gallagher, Patricia B. Kellogg, Heidi Schultz

IMAGE COLLECTION
Bill Bonner, Taranjit Kaur, Stephen St. John, Sanjeewa Wickramasekera

PRE-PRESS
David Bulebush, Clayton R. Burneston, Ernest J. Colantonio, Jr., Greg Doerning, Jacqueline Jackson, Andrew Jaecks, Leland N. Johnson, Ming Liu, Ann Marie Pelish, Eduardo Rubiano, Gene Shaffer, James Tyndall, David Uhl, Robert Weck, Jr., Warren Wilson

ENGRAVING AND PRINTING
Joseph M. Anderson, Vincent P. Ryan

ADVERTISING
Sean Flanagan, Stephen P. Giannetti, John Iavarone

MARKETING
Kitty Carroll Colbert, Aled Greville, John MacKethan

MAGAZINE PUBLISHING
John Q. Griffin, President, Magazine Group
Elizabeth Steckel

NATIONAL GEOGRAPHIC SOCIETY
Gilbert M. Grosvenor, Chairman
John M. Fahey, Jr., President and CEO

HOW TO CONTACT US
Call: 1-800-NGS-LINE
(1-800-647-5463)
Toll free from U.S., Canada,
8 a.m.-midnight ET, Mon.-Fri.
8:30 a.m.-7 p.m. ET, Sat.
For a free catalog call:
1-800-447-0647
Special device for the
hearing-impaired:
(TDD) 1-800-548-9797

Write:
National Geographic Society
PO Box 98199
Washington, DC 20090-8199
Internet: nationalgeographic.com

we have liftoff

SALUTING THE SPACE AGE, witnesses to the launch of moon-bound Apollo 11 shield their eyes from the Florida sun on July 16, 1969. Former President Lyndon B. Johnson and Ladybird Johnson stand shoulder to shoulder in the crowd as the giant Saturn V rocket thunders into the sky over the Kennedy Space Center. The couple were not alone in their awe. The world stood at attention that summer, entranced by the achievements and swift progress of the astronauts. Only eight years earlier, Soviet cosmonaut Yuri A. Gagarin had become the first human to venture into space, chased by a series of U.S. missions that made household names of astronauts like Alan Shepard, John Glenn, and Ed White. A full-blown space race was under way between the superpowers, and the finish line was the moon. Now three Americans were speeding toward the lunar surface for the first time. If the moon was within reach, why not Mars? If we could land on other worlds, why not live on them too? Earth was no longer a sealed blue bubble twirling through the void, but a base camp. A way point. A launchpad to the universe.

"This beast is best felt. Shake, rattle, and roll! We are thrown left and right. . . . It is steering like crazy . . . and I just hope it knows where it's going, because for the first ten seconds we are perilously close to that umbilical tower." —MICHAEL COLLINS, ASTRONAUT

As a Saturn V rocket's 7.6 million pounds of thrust lifts the Apollo 11 crew off the launch-pad, liquid oxygen vapor shrouds its first stage. "This Saturn gave us a magnificent ride," Neil Armstrong said.

Following pages: Not your average dashboard: The space shuttle's updated cockpit in-cludes 11 flat-panel liquid crystal dis-plays, replacing dials, gauges, and green cathode ray tube screens.

America's original rocket man

"Goddard's Invention Fails to Reach Objective by 238,856 ¾ Miles," teased the *Boston Herald* the day after a 1929 test by rocketry pioneer Robert Goddard. Earlier the *New York Times* had ridiculed him for proposing that a rocket could work in space and that man could reach the moon. Goddard, a physics professor at Clark University in Worcester, Massachusetts, "seems to lack the knowledge ladled out daily in high schools," the *Times* chided. The following year

Charles Lindbergh recommended Goddard to the Guggenheim family, who granted funds that enabled Goddard to set up a rocket workshop and test range in the desert near Roswell, New Mexico. There Goddard (left, adjusting a steering vane) developed the first gyroscopic rocket-guidance system, fired the first liquid-fueled rocket faster than sound, and routinely sent missiles more than a mile high from the launch tower (right). "It has often proved true," he once said, "that the dream of yesterday is the hope of today, and the reality of tomorrow." As Apollo II headed to the moon in 1969, the *Times* revisited its critique of Goddard's work: "It is now definitely established that a rocket can function in a vacuum as well as in an atmosphere," the newspaper wrote. "The *Times* regrets the error."

|

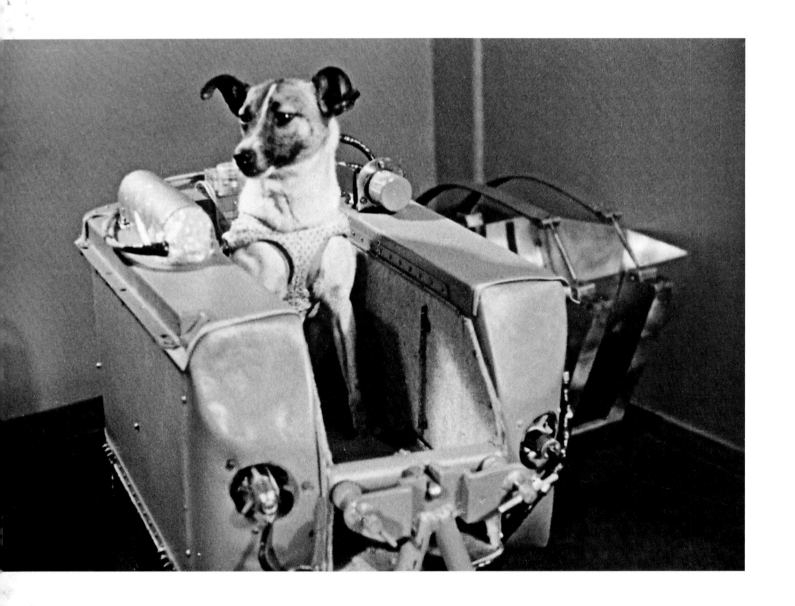

Dubbed "Muttnik" in the U.S. press, a Soviet dog named Laika (left) rode Sputnik 2 into space on November 3, 1957, becoming the first living creature in orbit. It is now believed she died hours after launch from overheating.

Valentina V. Tereshkova (below) trains for her 48-orbit flight June 16-19, 1963. A civilian parachuting enthusiast, she had worked in a Soviet textile plant before being chosen to become the first woman in space.

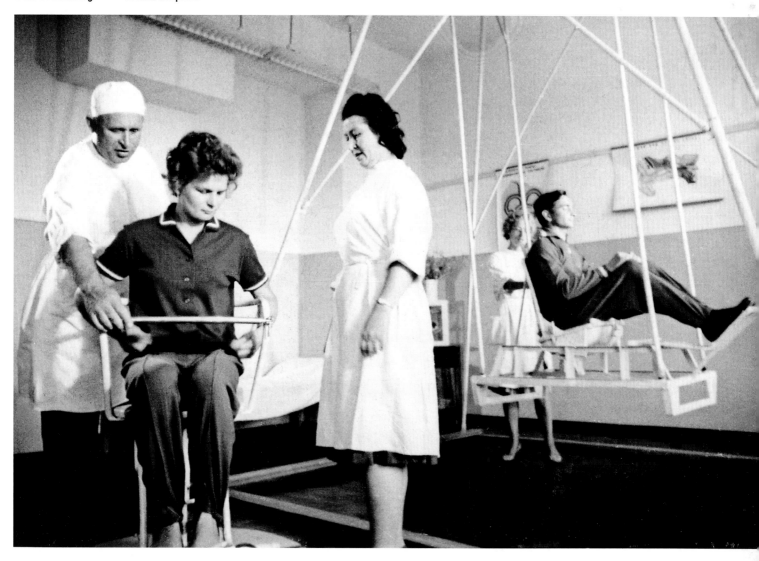

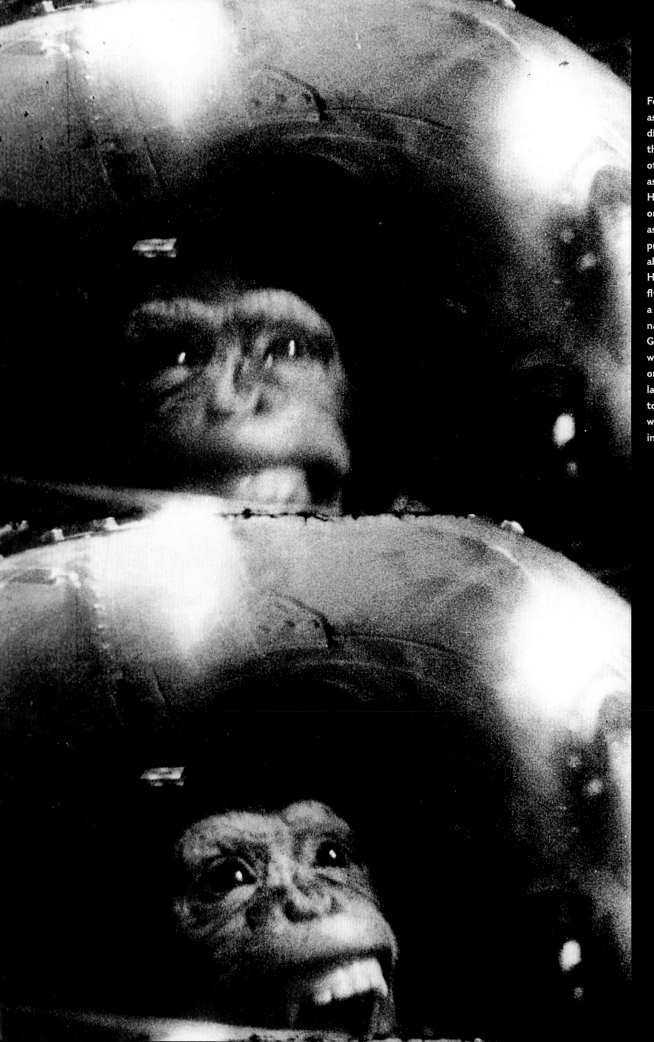

Feeling three times
as many g's as pre-
dicted—17 times
the normal force
of gravity—a NASA
astrochimp named
Ham bares his teeth
on January 31, 1961,
as a Mercury flight
propels him 156 miles
above the Earth.
Ham and other high-
flying animals blazed
a trail for U.S. astro-
nauts like John H.
Glenn, Jr. (right),
who braved the rig-
ors of liftoff a year
later. Glenn's flight
took him around the
world three times
in under five hours.

Carrying a portable air conditioner to cool his pressure suit, Alan B. Shepard, Jr. (right), strides across pad 5 at Cape Canaveral toward the Redstone rocket that would carry him on the first U.S. manned venture into space. His suborbital flight on May 5, 1961, took him to an altitude of 116.5 miles and lasted just 15 minutes before splashing down in the Atlantic.

Nine months later it was Glenn's turn to lift off from the forest of gantries in Florida (below).

ABOVE: NASA • RIGHT: WILLIAM TAUB, NASA

Floating dreamlike 100 miles above the Earth, Edward H. White II (left and above) becomes the first American to perform a space walk, on June 3, 1965. Maneuvering with a handheld gas gun, White traveled 6,000 miles from Hawaii to Bermuda in 21 minutes.

Preceding pages: Eyes on the prize, Alan Shepard watches technicians shut the hatch of his *Freedom 7* capsule. "Are you really ready?" a friend at the control center asked him privately. Shepard laughed and replied, "Go!"

One giant leap for mankind

Brilliantly lit by searchlights, the Saturn V rocket, crowned by the Apollo II spacecraft, shimmers on its launchpad at the Kennedy Space Center. The payload: three courageous astronauts. Two of them, Neil Armstrong and Edwin E. "Buzz" Aldrin, Jr., would become the first humans to walk on the moon on July 20, 1969. The third, Michael Collins, manned the orbiting command module. First came a dry run on Earth (opposite, top left) with Aldrin, at left, and Armstrong

practicing maneuvers in their space suits at the Manned Spacecraft Center in Houston. Later the two made the trip to the moon's surface and back to lunar orbit in the *Eagle* (center left). During their 22 hours on the moon they planted the Stars and Stripes on the Sea of Tranquillity (top right). Aldrin photographed a footprint in the dust, which resembled powdered charcoal (center right). After splashdown in the Pacific, the astronauts were taken aboard the aircraft carrier U.S.S. *Hornet* and presented with a three-stage rocket cake (bottom left). On this day, they couldn't have it or eat it too, as they were quarantined for 2.5 weeks to guard against contamination of the Earth by alien organisms —a concern that proved groundless. Lunar grime and fatigue color Eugene A. Cernan's face (bottom right) after a moonwalk on Apollo 17 in December 1972, the last of the six moon landings. With that mission—the astronauts spent a record three days on the surface and 22 hours outside the lander—what had been one small step for Armstrong had turned into a routine stroll for II others.

ABOVE: OTIS IMBODEN • OPPOSITE: RALPH MORSE, *LIFE* (TOP LEFT) • MICHAEL COLLINS, NASA (CENTER LEFT) • NASA

■ Send this image (top right) as an e-greeting and watch man's first steps on the moon at nationalgeographic.com/magazine/space.

space firsts

Dates refer to launches:

Charles Duke appears twice in a mosaic of photos taken by John Young during Apollo 16 in April 1972 (above). The pair drove 16.8 miles in three trips in the lunar rover, at center.

Sputnik I
10/4/57 First artificial satellite

Explorer I
2/1/58 First U.S. satellite, discovers Van Allen radiation belts

SCORE
12/18/58 First orbital communications satellite

Luna 2
9/12/59 First spacecraft to strike another world, impacts moon 9/14/59

Tiros I
4/1/60 First weather satellite

Vostok I
4/12/61 Yuri Gagarin, first human in space, completes one full orbit of Earth

Freedom 7
5/5/61 Alan Shepard, first American in space

Vostok 2
8/6/61 Gherman Titov, first human to spend a day, and to sleep, in space

Friendship 7
2/20/62 John Glenn, first American in orbit

Telstar I
7/10/62 First private communications satellite

Vostok 3 and 4
8/11/62, 8/15/62 First mission of two humans, and two craft, in orbit

Mariner 2
8/27/62 Discovers solar wind; first Venus flyby

Vostok 6
6/16/63 Valentina Tereshkova, first woman in space

Ranger 7
7/28/64 First close-up images of lunar surface

Voskhod I
10/12/64 First spacecraft to carry more than one person (crew of three includes first physician in space)

Mariner 4
11/28/64 First Mars flyby

Gemini 3
3/23/65 First American two-person crew

Venera 3
11/16/65 First Venus probe

Asterix
11/26/65 First French-launched satellite

Luna 9
1/31/66 First spacecraft to land on moon, takes first photos from surface

First a trickle, then a torrent of humans has flowed into space—438 so far, by the U.S. Air Force's yardstick of reaching 50 miles in altitude. Among this total, eight were X-15 rocket plane pilots flying brief, suborbital missions in the 1960s. Others, like Apollo 16's Charles Duke, found a way to take the family along to the moon (left).

1961 Yuri Gagarin · Alan Shepard · Virgil Grissom · Gherman Titov 1962 John Glenn · Scott Carpenter · Robert White · Andrian Nikolayev · Pavel Popovich · Walter Schirra 1963 Joe Walker · Gordon Cooper · Valery Bykovsky · Valentina Tereshkova · Robert Rushworth 1964 Vladimir Komarov · Konstantin Feoktistov · Boris Yegorov 1965 Pavel Belyayev · Alexei Leonov · Virgil Grissom · John Young · James McDivitt · Edward White · Joe Engle · Gordon Cooper · Charles Conrad · John McKay · Frank Borman · James Lovell · Walter Schirra · Thomas Stafford 1966 Neil Armstrong · David Scott · Thomas Stafford · Eugene Cernan · John Young · Michael Collins · Charles Conrad · Richard Gordon · Bill Dana · James Lovell · Edwin Aldrin 1967 Vladimir Komarov · Pete Knight · Mike Adams 1968 Walter Schirra · Donn Eisele · Walter Cunningham · Georgi Beregovoy · Bill Dana · Frank Borman · James Lovell · William Anders 1969 Vladimir Shatalov · Boris Volynov · Alexei Yeliseyev · Yevgeny Khrunov · James McDivitt · David Scott · Russell Schweickart · Thomas Stafford · John Young · Eugene Cernan · Neil Armstrong · Michael Collins · Edwin Aldrin · Georgy Shonin · Valery Kubasov · Anatoly Filipchenko · Viktor Gorbatko · Vladislav Volkov · Charles Conrad · Richard Gordon · Alan Bean 1970 James Lovell · Fred Haise · John Swigert · Andrian Nikolayev · Vitaly Sevastianov 1971 Alan Shepard · Stuart Roosa · Edgar Mitchell · Vladimir Shatalov · Alexei Yeliseyev · Nikolai Rukavishnikov · Georgi Dobrovolosky · Vladislav Volkov · Viktor Patsayev · David Scott · Alfred Worden · James Irwin 1972 John Young · Charles Duke · Thomas Mattingly · Eugene Cernan · Harrison Schmitt · Ronald Evans 1973 Charles Conrad · Joseph Kerwin · Paul Weitz · Alan Bean · Jack Lousma · Owen Garriott · Vasily Lazarev · Oleg Makarov · Gerald Carr · Edward Gibson · William Pogue · Pyotr Klimuk · Valentin Lebedev 1974 Pavel Popovich · Yuri Artyukhin · Gennadi Sarafanov · Lev Demin · Anatoly Filipchenko · Nikolai Rukavishnikov 1975 Alexei Gubarev · Georgy Grechko · Vasily Lazarev · Oleg Makarov · Pyotr Klimuk · Vitaliy Sevastyanov · Alexei Leonov · Valery Kubasov · Thomas Stafford · Donald Slayton · Vance Brand 1976 Boris Volynov · Vitaly Zholobov · Valery Bykovsky · Vladimir Aksenov · Vyacheslav Zudov · Valery Rozhdestvensky 1977 Viktor Gorbatko · Yuri Glazkov · Vladimir Kovalenok · Valery Ryumin · Yuri Romanenko · Georgy Grechko 1978 Vladimir Dzhanibekov · Oleg Makarov · Alexei Gubarev · Vladimir Remek · Vladimir Kovalenok · Alexander Ivanchenkov · Pyotr Klimuk · Miroslaw Hermaszewski · Valery Bykovsky · Sigmund Jaehn 1979 Vladimir Lyakhov · Valery Ryumin · Nikolai Rukavishnikov · Georgy Ivanov 1980 Leonid Popov · Valery Ryumin · Valery Kubasov · Bertalan Farkas · Yuri Malyshev · Vladimir Aksenov · Viktor Gorbatko · Pham Tuan · Yuri Romanenko · Arnaldo Tamayo Mendez · Leonid Kizim · Oleg Makarov · Gennady Strekalov 1981 Vladimir Kovalenok · Viktor Savinykh · Vladimir Dzhanibekov · Jugderdemidiyn Gurragcha · John Young · Robert Crippen · Leonid Popov · Dumitru Prunariu · Joe Engle · Richard Truly 1982 Jack Lousma · Gordon Fullerton · Anatoly Berezovoy · Valentin Lebedev · Vladimir Dzhanibekov · Alexander Ivanchenkov · Jean-Loup Chrétien · Thomas Mattingly · Henry Hartsfield · Leonid Popov · Alexander Serebrov · Svetlana Savitskaya · Vance Brand · Robert Overmyer · Joseph Allen · William Lenoir 1983 Paul Weitz · Karol Bobko · Donald Peterson · Story Musgrave · Vladimir Titov · Gennady Strekalov · Alexander Serebrov · Robert Crippen · Frederick Hauck · John Fabian · Sally Ride · Norman Thagard · Vladimir Lyakhov · Alexander Alexanderov · Richard Truly · Daniel Brandenstein · Dale Gardner · Guion Bluford · William Thornton · John Young · Brewster Shaw · Owen Garriott · Robert Parker · Byron Lichtenberg · Ulf Merbold 1984 Vance Brand · Robert Gibson · Bruce McCandless · Ronald McNair · Robert Stewart · Leonid Kizim · Vladimir Solovyov · Oleg Atkov · Yuri Malyshev · Gennady Strekalov · Rakesh Sharma · Robert Crippen · Francis Scobee · Terry Hart · George Nelson · James van Hoften · Vladimir Dzhanibekov · Svetlana Savitskaya · Igor Volk · Henry Hartsfield · Michael Coats · Richard Mullane · Steve Hawley · Judith Resnik · Charles Walker · Jon McBride · Kathryn Sullivan · Sally Ride · David Leestma · Paul Scully-Power · Marc Garneau · Frederick Hauck · David Walker · Joseph Allen · Anna Fisher · Dale Gardner 1985 Thomas Mattingly · Loren Shriver · Ellison Onizuka · James Buchli · Gary Payton · Karol Bobko · Donald Williams · Rhea Seddon · David Griggs · Jeffrey Hoffman · Charles Walker · Jake Garn · Robert Overmyer · Frederick Gregory · Don Lind · Norman Thagard · William Thornton · Lodewijk van den Berg · Taylor Wang · Vladimir Dzhanibekov · Viktor Savinykh · Daniel Brandenstein · John Creighton · Shannon Lucid · John Fabian · Steven Nagel · Patrick Baudry · Prince Sultan Salman Al-Saud · Gordon Fullerton · Roy Bridges · Karl Henize · Anthony England · Story Musgrave · Loren Acton · John-David Bartoe · Joe Engle · Richard Covey · James van Hoften · William Fisher · Mike Lounge · Vladimir Vasyutin · Georgy Grechko · Alexander Volkov · Karol Bobko · Ronald Grabe · Robert Stewart · David Hilmers · William Pailes · Henry Hartsfield · Steven Nagel · Bonnie Dunbar · James Buchli · Guion Bluford · Ernst Messerschmid · Reinhard Furrer · Wubbo Ockels · Brewster Shaw · Bryan O'Connor · Mary Cleave · Sherwood Spring · Jerry Ross · Rodolfo Neri Vela · Charles Walker 1986 Robert Gibson · Charles Bolden · Franklin Chang-Díaz · Steve Hawley · George Nelson · Robert Cenker · Bill Nelson · Leonid Kizim · Vladimir Solovyov 1987 Yuri Romanenko · Alexander Laveikin · Alexander Viktorenko · Alexander Alexanderov · Mohammed Faris · Vladimir Titov · Musa Manarov · Anatoly Levchenko 1988 Viktor Savinykh · Anatoly Solovyev · Alexander Alexanderov · Vladimir Lyakhov · Valery Polyakov · Abbdul Mohmand · Frederick Hauck · Richard Covey · Mike Lounge · David Hilmers · George Nelson · Alexander Volkov · Sergei Krikalev · Jean-Loup Chrétien · Robert Gibson · Guy Gardner · Richard Mullane · Jerry Ross · William Shepherd 1989 Michael Coats · John Blaha · James Bagian · James Buchli · Robert Springer · David Walker · Ronald Grabe · Norman Thagard · Mary Cleave · Mark Lee · Brewster Shaw · Richard Richards · James Adamson · David Leestma · Mark Brown · Alexander Viktorenko · Alexander Serebrov · Donald Williams · Michael McCulley · Shannon Lucid · Franklin Chang-Díaz · Ellen Baker · Frederick Gregory · Kathryn Thornton · Story Musgrave · Manley Carter 1990 Daniel Brandenstein · James Wetherbee · Bonnie Dunbar · Marsha Ivins · David Low · Anatoly Solovyev · Alexander Balandin · John Creighton · John Casper · David Hilmers · Richard Mullane · Pierre Thuot · Loren Shriver · Charles Bolden · Steve Hawley · Bruce McCandless · Kathryn Sullivan · Gennady Manakov · Gennady Strekalov · Richard Richards · Robert Cabana · Bruce Melnick · William Shepherd · Thomas Akers · Richard Covey · Frank Culbertson · Charles Gemar · Robert Springer · Carl Meade · Vance Brand · Guy Gardner · Jeffrey Hoffman · Mike Lounge · Robert Parker · Samuel Durrance · Ronald Parise · Viktor Afanasyev · Musa Manarov · Toyohiro Akiyama 1991 Steven Nagel · Kenneth Cameron · Linda Godwin · Jerry Ross · Jay Apt · Michael Coats · Blaine Hammond · Gregory Harbaugh · Donald McMonagle · Guion Bluford · Charles Veach · Richard Hieb · Anatoly Artsebarsky · Sergei Krikalev · Helen Sharman · Bryan O'Connor · Sidney Gutierrez · James Bagian · Tamara Jernigan · Rhea Seddon · Drew Gaffney · Millie Hughes-Fulford ·

the right stuff

■ Hear President Nixon's historic phone call to the Apollo 11 crew at nationalgeographic.com/magazine/space.

Surveyor I
5/30/66 First craft to soft-land on moon

Intelsat 2B
1/11/67 Completes global cluster of satellites that enables instant worldwide communications

Apollo 11
7/16/69 Neil Armstrong, first human to walk on moon

Apollo 12
11/14/69 Second manned lunar landing, walking distance from Surveyor 3 site

Luna 17
11/10/70 First unmanned rover lands on moon, travels across surface

Soyuz 11
6/6/71 First crew to occupy Salyut 1, first orbiting space station; after 24 days in orbit, crew dies during reentry

Apollo 15
7/26/71 Fourth manned lunar landing, first to drive rover

Apollo 16
4/16/72 Fifth manned lunar landing

Landsat I
7/23/72 First satellite dedicated to studying Earth and its resources

Skylab
5/14/73 First U.S. orbiting space station

Mariner 10
11/3/73 Takes first close-up photos of Mercury

Venera 9
6/8/75 First images from surface of Venus

Voyager 1
9/5/77 Discovers volcanoes on Io during flyby of Jupiter

Soyuz 35
4/9/80 Delivers cosmonauts to Salyut 6 for 185-day mission

Apollo 1
1/27/67 Launch-pad fire kills astronauts Grissom, White, and Chaffee

Apollo 8
12/21/68 First

Ohsumi
2/11/70 First Japanese-launched satellite

Apollo 13
4/11/70 Lunar mission aborted when oxygen tank

Apollo 14
1/31/71 Third manned lunar landing, first in mountains

Mariner 9
5/30/71 First successful orbital

Prospero
10/28/71 First British-launched satellite

Pioneer 10
3/3/72 First spacecraft to fly by Jupiter

Apollo 17
12/7/72 Sixth and final manned lunar landing

Pioneer 11
4/6/73 Takes first close-up images of Saturn

Viking 1
8/20/75 First soft landing on Mars

Voyager 2
8/20/77 First flyby of Uranus and Neptune, af-

Rohini 1B
7/18/80 First Indian-launched satellite

Columbia (STS 1)
4/12/81 First flight of space shuttle

39

Soyuz T5
5/13/82
**Delivers crew
to Salyut 7, sets
new record of 211
days, grows first
plants from seeds
in space**

Challenger (STS 7)
**6/18/83
Sally Ride, first
American woman
in space**

Mir
**2/20/86 Core
module is
launched for
space station**

Ofeq I
**9/19/88
First Israeli-
launched satellite**

Buran
**11/15/88 First
and only flight
of Soviet space
shuttle**

Discovery (STS 31)
**4/24/90
Deploys Hubble
Space Telescope**

Soyuz TM11
**12/2/90 Journal-
ist Toyohiro Aki-
yama, first paying
passenger in orbit**

Soyuz TM18
**1/8/94 Valery
Polyakov sets
record of 437
consecutive days
in orbit**

Columbia (STS
93) **7/23/99 Ei-
leen Collins, first
U.S. woman to
command mission**

Soyuz TM31
**10/31/00 First
crew occupies
International
Space Station**

WMAP
**6/30/01 Tele-
scope studies
cosmic back-
ground radiation**

Pioneer 10
**Last transmission
from probe 7.6
billion miles away
on 1/23/03**

Columbia (STS
107) **2/1/03
Shuttle breaks up
during reentry;
crew of seven lost**

MERs
**6/10/03, 7/7/03
Mars rovers Spir-
it and Opportu-
nity, scheduled to
arrive in 1/04**

Vega I
**12/15/84 First
craft to make
close approach to
Halley's comet**

Challenger (STS
25) **1/28/86
Explosion kills
crew of seven**

COBE
**11/18/89
Satellite mea-
sures cosmic
microwave back-
ground radiation**

Mars Pathfinder
**12/4/96 First
Mars rover,
Sojourner**

Cassini/Huygens
**10/15/97 Expect-
ed to orbit Saturn
7/04, probe to
land on Titan
1/05**

Mir
**Space station
falls to Earth
3/23/01, burns
up over Pacific**

Soyuz TM32
**4/28/01 Dennis
Tito, first space
tourist**

Mars Express/
Beagle 2
**6/2/03 First
European Mars
effort, orbiter
and lander set
to arrive on
12/25/03**

SMART I
**9/27/03 Euro-
pean Space Agen-
cy lunar orbiter,
scheduled to
arrive early 2005**

PHOTO: NASA • **TIME LINE:** ROBERT ZIMMERMAN, *THE CHRONOLOGICAL ENCYCLOPEDIA OF DISCOVERIES IN SPACE*

John Blaha · Michael Baker · Shannon Lucid · David Low · James Adamson · John Creighton · Kenneth Reightler · Charles Gemar · James Buchli · Mark Brown · Alexander Volkov · Toktar Aubakirov · Franz Viehboeck · Frederick Gregory · Terence Henricks · James Voss · Story Musgrave · Mario Runco · Tom Hennen 1992 Ronald Grabe · Stephen Oswald · Norman Thagard · David Hilmers · William Readdy · Roberta Bondar · Ulf Merbold · Alexander Viktorenko · Alexander Kaleri · Klaus-Dietrich Flade · Charles Bolden · Brian Duffy · Kathryn Sullivan · David Leestma · Michael Foale · Dirk Frimout · Byron Lichtenberg · Daniel Brandenstein · Kevin Chilton · Richard Hieb · Bruce Melnick · Pierre Thuot · Kathryn Thornton · Thomas Akers · Richard Richards · Kenneth Bowersox · Bonnie Dunbar · Ellen Baker · Carl Meade · Larry DeLucas · Eugene Trinh · Anatoly Solovyev · Sergei Avdeyev · Michel Tognini · Loren Shriver · Andrew Allen · Claude Nicollier · Marsha Ivins · Jeffrey Hoffman · Franklin Chang-Díaz · Franco Malerba · Robert Gibson · Curt Brown · Mark Lee · Jay Apt · Jan Davis · Mae Jemison · Mamoru Mohri · James Wetherbee · Michael Baker · William Shepherd · Tamara Jernigan · Charles Veach · Steve MacLean · David Walker · Robert Cabana · Guion Bluford · James Voss · Rich Clifford 1993 John Casper · Donald McMonagle · Gregory Harbaugh · Mario Runco · Susan Helms · Gennady Manakov · Alexander Poleshchuk · Kenneth Cameron · Stephen Oswald · Michael Foale · Kenneth Cockrell · Ellen Ochoa · Steven Nagel · Terence Henricks · Jerry Ross · Charles Precourt · Bernard Harris · Ulrich Walter · Hans Schlegel · Ronald Grabe · Brian Duffy · David Low · Nancy Sherlock · Jess Wisoff · Janice Voss · Vasily Tsibliyev · Alexander Serebrov · Jean-Pierre Haigneré · Frank Culbertson · William Readdy · James Newman · Daniel Bursch · Carl Walz · John Blaha · Richard Searfoss · Shannon Lucid · David Wolf · William McArthur · Martin Fettman · Richard Covey · Kenneth Bowersox · Thomas Akers · Jeffrey Hoffman · Kathryn Thornton · Claude Nicollier · Story Musgrave 1994 Viktor Afanasyev · Yuri Usachev · Valery Polyakov · Charles Bolden · Kenneth Reightler · Jan Davis · Ronald Sega · Franklin Chang-Díaz · Sergei Krikalev · John Casper · Andrew Allen · Pierre Thuot · Charles Gemar · Marsha Ivins · Sidney Gutierrez · Kevin Chilton · Jay Apt · Rich Clifford · Linda Godwin · Thomas Jones · Yuri Malenchenko · Talgat Musabayev · Robert Cabana · James Halsell · Richard Hieb · Carl Walz · Leroy Chiao · Donald Thomas · Chiaki Mukai · Richard Richards · Blaine Hammond · Jerry Linenger · Susan Helms · Carl Meade · Mark Lee · Michael Baker · Terrence Wilcutt · Thomas Jones · Steven Smith · Daniel Bursch · Jess Wisoff · Alexander Viktorenko · Elena Kondakova · Ulf Merbold · Donald McMonagle · Curt Brown · Ellen Ochoa · Joseph Tanner · Jean-François Clervoy · Scott Parazynski 1995 James Wetherbee · Eileen Collins · Bernard Harris · Michael Foale · Janice Voss · Vladimir Titov · Stephen Oswald · William Gregory · John Grunsfeld · Wendy Lawrence · Tamara Jernigan · Ronald Parise · Samuel Durrance · Vladimir Dezhurov · Gennady Strekalov · Norman Thagard · Robert Gibson · Charles Precourt · Ellen Baker · Gregory Harbaugh · Bonnie Dunbar · Anatoly Solovyev · Nikolai Budarin · Terence Henricks · Kevin Kregel · Nancy Currie · Donald Thomas · Mary Ellen Weber · Yuri Gidzenko · Sergei Avdeyev · Thomas Reiter · David Walker · Kenneth Cockrell · James Voss · James Newman · Michael Gernhardt · Kenneth Bowersox · Kent Rominger · Catherine Coleman · Michael Lopez-Alegria · Kathryn Thornton · Fred Leslie · Albert Sacco · Kenneth Cameron · James Halsell · Chris Hadfield · Jerry Ross · William McArthur 1996 Brian Duffy · Brent Jett · Leroy Chiao · Winston Scott · Koichi Wakata · Daniel Barry · Yuri Onufrienko · Yuri Usachev · Andrew Allen · Scott Horowitz · Jeffrey Hoffman · Maurizio Cheli · Claude Nicollier · Franklin Chang-Díaz · Umberto Guidoni · Kevin Chilton · Richard Searfoss · Linda Godwin · Rich Clifford · Ronald Sega · Shannon Lucid · John Casper · Curt Brown · Andrew Thomas · Daniel Bursch · Mario Runco · Marc Garneau · Terence Henricks · Kevin Kregel · Richard Linnehan · Susan Helms · Charles Brady · Jean-Jacques Favier · Robert Thirsk · Claudie André-Deshays · Valery Korzun · Alexander Kaleri · William Readdy · Terrence Wilcutt · Jay Apt · Thomas Akers · Carl Walz · John Blaha · Kenneth Cockrell · Kent Rominger · Tamara Jernigan · Thomas Jones · Story Musgrave 1997 Michael Baker · Brent Jett · Jess Wisoff · John Grunsfeld · Marsha Ivins · Jerry Linenger · Vasily Tsibliyev · Alexander Lazutkin · Reinhold Ewald · Kenneth Bowersox · Scott Horowitz · Joseph Tanner · Steve Hawley · Gregory Harbaugh · Mark Lee · Steven Smith · James Halsell · Susan Kilrain · Janice Voss · Michael Gernhardt · Donald Thomas · Roger Crouch · Gregory Linteris · Charles Precourt · Eileen Collins · Jean-François Clervoy · Carlos Noriega · Edward Lu · Elena Kondakova · Michael Foale · Anatoly Solovyev · Pavel Vinogradov · Curt Brown · Kent Rominger · Jan Davis · Robert Curbeam · Stephen Robinson · Bjarni Tryggvason · James Wetherbee · Michael Bloomfield · Scott Parazynski · Vladimir Titov · Jean-Loup Chrétien · Wendy Lawrence · David Wolf · Kevin Kregel · Steven Lindsey · Kalpana Chawla · Winston Scott · Takao Doi · Leonid Kadenyuk 1998 Terrence Wilcutt · Joe Edwards · James Reilly · Michael Anderson · Bonnie Dunbar · Salizhan Sharipov · Andrew Thomas · Talgat Musabayev · Nikolai Budarin · Leopold Eyharts · Richard Searfoss · Scott Altman · Richard Linnehan · Kay Hire · Dafydd Williams · Jay Buckey · James Pawelczyk · Charles Precourt · Dominic Gorie · Franklin Chang-Díaz · Wendy Lawrence · Janet Kavandi · Valery Ryumin · Gennady Padalka · Sergei Avdeyev · Yuri Baturin · Curt Brown · Steven Lindsey · Scott Parazynski · Stephen Robinson · Pedro Duque · Chiaki Mukai · John Glenn · Robert Cabana · Frederick Sturckow · James Newman · Nancy Currie · Jerry Ross · Sergei Krikalev 1999 Viktor Afanasyev · Jean-Pierre Haigneré · Ivan Bella · Kent Rominger · Rick Husband · Daniel Barry · Valery Tokarev · Ellen Ochoa · Julie Payette · Tamara Jernigan · Eileen Collins · Jeff Ashby · Michel Tognini · Steve Hawley · Catherine Coleman · Curt Brown · Scott Kelly · Steven Smith · Michael Foale · John Grunsfeld · Claude Nicollier · Jean-François Clervoy 2000 Kevin Kregel · Dominic Gorie · Gerhard Thiele · Janet Kavandi · Janice Voss · Mamoru Mohri · Sergei Zalyotin · Alexander Kaleri · James Halsell · Scott Horowitz · Susan Helms · Yuri Usachev · James Voss · Mary Ellen Weber · Jeffrey Williams · Terrence Wilcutt · Scott Altman · Daniel Burbank · Ed Lu · Yuri Malenchenko · Rick Mastracchio · Boris Morukov · Brian Duffy · Pamela Melroy · Leroy Chiao · William McArthur · Jess Wisoff · Michael Lopez-Alegria · Koichi Wakata · William Shepherd · Yuri Gidzenko · Sergei Krikalev · Brent Jett · Michael Bloomfield · Joseph Tanner · Marc Garneau · Carlos Noriega 2001 Kenneth Cockrell · Mark Polansky · Robert Curbeam · Marsha Ivins · Thomas Jones · James Wetherbee · James Kelly · Andrew Thomas · Paul Richards · James Voss · Susan Helms · Yuri Usachev · Kent Rominger · Jeff Ashby · Chris Hadfield · John Phillips · Scott Parazynski · Umberto Guidoni · Yuri Lonchakov · Talgat Musabayev · Yuri Baturin · Dennis Tito · Steven Lindsey · Charles Hobaugh · Michael Gernhardt · Janet Kavandi · James Reilly · Scott Horowitz · Frederick Sturckow · Patrick Forrester · Daniel Barry · Frank Culbertson · Vladimir Dezhurov · Mikhail Turin · Viktor Afanasyev · Konstantin Kozeev · Claudie Haigneré · Dominic Gorie · Mark Kelly · Linda Godwin · Daniel Tani · Yuri Onufrienko · Carl Walz · Daniel Bursch 2002 Scott Altman · Duane Carey · John Grunsfeld · Nancy Currie · James Newman · Richard Linnehan · Michael Massimino · Michael Bloomfield · Stephen Frick · Jerry Ross · Steven Smith · Ellen Ochoa · Lee Morin · Rex Walheim · Yuri Gidzenko · Roberto Vittori · Mark Shuttleworth · Kenneth Cockrell · Paul Lockhart · Franklin Chang-Díaz · Philippe Perrin · Valery Korzun · Peggy Whitson · Sergei Treschev · Jeff Ashby · Pamela Melroy · David Wolf · Piers Sellers · Sandra Magnus · Fyodor Yurchikhin · Sergei Zalyotin · Frank De Winne · Yuri Lonchakov · James Wetherbee · Paul Lockhart · Michael Lopez-Alegria · John Herrington · Kenneth Bowersox · Nikolai Budarin · Donald Pettit 2003 Rick Husband · William McCool · Michael Anderson · Kalpana Chawla · David Brown · Laurel Clark · Ilan Ramon · Yuri Malenchenko · Ed Lu · Yang Liwei · Michael Foale · Alexander Kaleri · Pedro Duque

PHOTO: NASA · NAMES: MARK WADE, ENCYCLOPEDIA ASTRONAUTICA, ASTRONAUTIX.COM; DAVID BAKER, JANE'S SPACE DIRECTORY; NASA

Flower-decked dancers stand ready to perform as the Apollo 14 astronauts arrive in American Samoa in February 1971, following another successful voyage to the moon. With the end of the Apollo program three missions later, a chapter in spaceflight ended—no humans have left Earth's orbit since.

|

Soviets build a mighty space machine

"Humanity will not remain on the Earth forever," wrote Konstantin Tsiolkovsky, father of Soviet space exploration, in 1911, "but in the pursuit of light and space will, at first timidly, penetrate beyond the limits of the atmosphere, and then will conquer all the space around the sun." Less than 50 years later, the first part of his dream began to come true when the Soviets launched Sputnik I, the first artificial satellite, into orbit on October 4, 1957. The beeping of the first spacecraft, heard round the world, caused fear in some and wonder in others, and sparked the space race between the Soviet Union and the United States. A Soviet stallion in that race, and one that refuses to go to pasture, a Soyuz rocket (left) takes a train to the Baikonur Cosmodrome launchpad in Kazakhstan where it hoisted the final team of cosmonauts to the aging Mir space station in April 2000. Shrouded in secrecy during the Soviet years, the Russian space program eventually opened up and is now collaborating with several European nations, Japan, and the U.S. on the International Space Station. Another Soyuz (right) blasts off for that station in October 2001, having become a taxi and lifeboat for crews of the orbiting outpost, a step toward fulfilling the second part of Tsiolkovsky's vision —to conquer all the space around the sun.

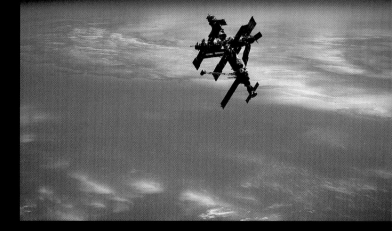

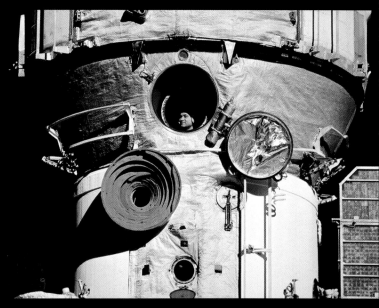

Upholding a tradition started by Yuri Gagarin, the first person in space, two cosmonauts relieve themselves on the tire of their transport bus. Before his 1961 flight, Gagarin did the same during an unplanned pit stop prior to takeoff. Since then, nearly every cosmonaut has followed suit.

Two hundred fifty miles above the Earth, space station Mir (top right) introduced an era of international cooperation. Cosmonaut Valery Polyakov (right) gazes from the station that hosted more than a hundred visitors from 12 countries. Designed to last five years, Mir survived 15 before being abandoned and plunging to Earth on March 23, 2001.

Weakened but cheerful, cosmonaut Valery Polyakov catches a lift home on March 22, 1995, after spending a world record 437 consecutive days in space. A physician, Polyakov used his stay on Mir to study the effects of prolonged exposure to zero gravity on the body. Despite some bone density loss, he proved that, with exercises, space crews could manage the negative effects of weightlessness on a round-trip to Mars, which could take as long as three years.

MOST DAYS IN SPACE

1. Sergei Avdeyev, Russia, 747.6
2. Valery Polyakov, Russia, 678.7
3. Anatoly Solovyev, Russia, 651
4. Sergei Krikalev, Russia, 624.4
5. Viktor Afanasyev, Russia, 555.8
28. Michael Foale, 257 (Foale, the U.S. record holder, was on the space station at press time. If he stays until April as planned, he will move to 17th and his Russian crewmate, Alexander Kaleri, will move to 5th.)

Facing the unthinkable

Disbelief darkens the expression of flight director Jay Greene (left) seconds after space shuttle *Challenger* exploded on January 28, 1986, killing all seven crew members. His stunned colleague Alan Briscoe stares at a monitor screen inside Houston's Mission Control as the orbiter becomes a ball of flame and smoke 73 seconds after launch (opposite, bottom right), its solid rocket boosters careening wildly away. The disaster was triggered by an eroded O-ring in the right booster that allowed hot gases to escape and ignite the main fuel tank. A 10-by-16-foot segment of *Challenger*'s right wing (top right) was pulled from waters 14 miles northeast of Cape Canaveral. In an earlier accident, Apollo 1 astronauts Roger B. Chaffee, Ed White, and Virgil I. "Gus" Grissom (bottom left, from left) perished on January 27, 1967, when a blaze ignited in their oxygen-rich command module (top left) during a preflight test. Three months later Soviet cosmonaut Vladimir Komarov was killed when his Soyuz I capsule crashed on landing. Soyuz II cosmonauts Georgi Dobrovolosky, Vladislav Volkov, and Viktor Patsayev also died during reentry, on June 29, 1971.

    NASA (ALL) • PRECEDING PAGES: MARSEL GUBAIDULLIN

"The same Creator who names the stars also knows the names of the seven souls we mourn today. The crew of the shuttle *Columbia* did not return safely to Earth; yet we can pray that all are safely home."

—PRESIDENT GEORGE W. BUSH

Columbia was completing its 28th mission on the morning of February I, 2003, when it disintegrated across the Texas sky (below), spewing debris over much of the state and western Louisiana. A portrait of the seven astronauts (below left) was processed from a roll of film found in the wreckage. (Clockwise from left: Kalpana Chawla, David M. Brown, William C. McCool, Michael P. Anderson, Ilan Ramon, Laurel Blair Salton Clark, and Rick D. Husband.) The first shuttle to fly into orbit, *Columbia* underwent final preparations at the Kennedy Space Center in 1980 (opposite) before its maiden flight in April 1981.

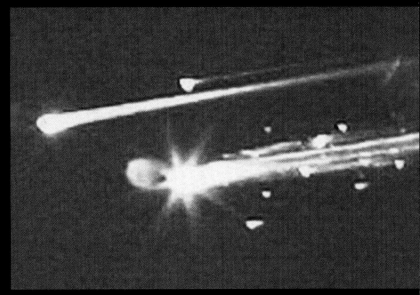

Some of the 84,000 pieces of *Columbia* recovered by searchers are spread out inside a hangar at the Kennedy Space Center. More than 25,000 workers combed parts of Texas and Louisiana looking for debris. A seven-month investigation found that super-heated air entered the left wing through a breach suffered during launch. New safety measures for a return to flight planned for later this year include a 50-foot extension boom stowed in the cargo bay that will allow astronauts in orbit to maneuver a camera around the exterior of the shuttle to look for potentially fatal chinks in the space-craft's armor.

NASA

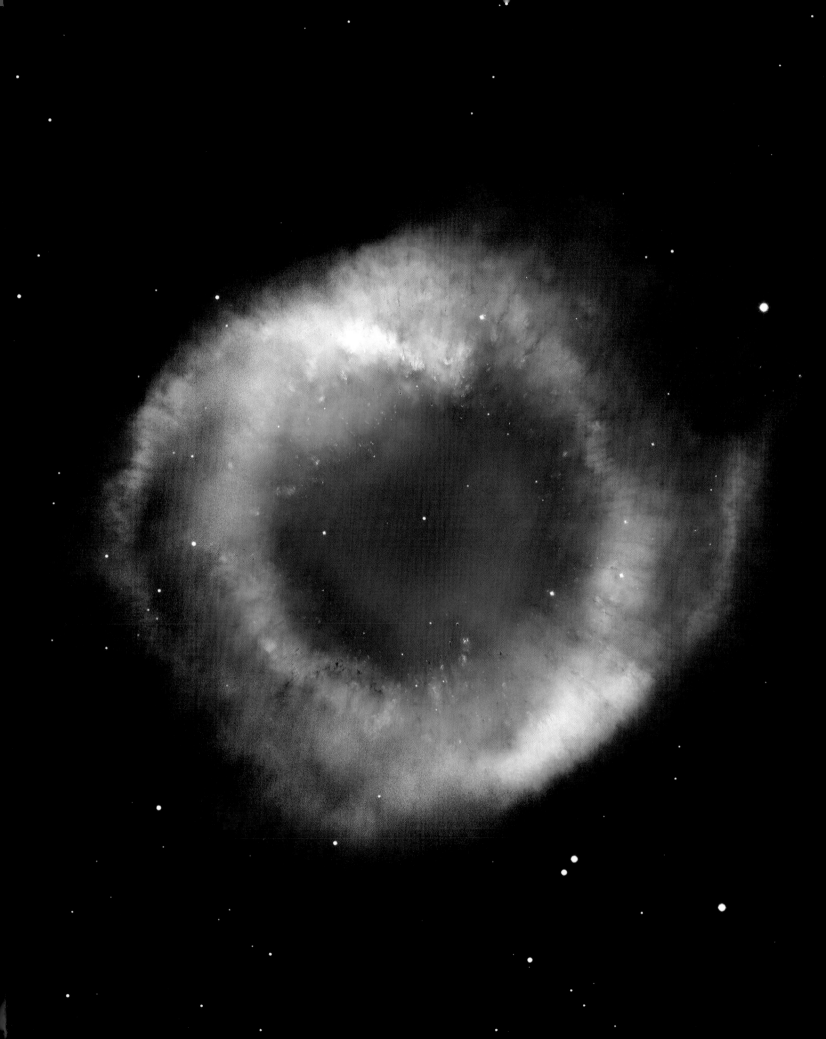

the shoreless cosmos

SINCE THE DAWN OF HUMAN AWARENESS people have wondered about the stars, prayed to them, navigated by them, conjured stories about them, and charted their movements. But the moment Galileo squinted through a novel new instrument—two glass lenses aligned in a lead tube—and spotted Jupiter's moons in 1610, our view of the heavens changed forever.

As telescopes got bigger, we got smaller. We learned that our galaxy is just one of a hundred billion—each with many billions of stars—and that the universe, far from orderly, is a chaotic expanse of violent collisions, collapses, and explosions. Our vision took a huge leap in 1990 with the launch of the Hubble Space Telescope. What appears to be an angry eye at left, for example, is the Helix Nebula, a trillion-mile-long tunnel of glowing gases pointed at Earth—one of 25,000 objects Hubble has inspected from its orbit 380 miles up. The next generation of space telescopes may allow us to peer even deeper into the universe, perhaps back to its very beginnings. In the meantime, we'll watch—and wonder.

■ Test your knowledge of our cosmos at nationalgeographic.com/magazine/space.

galaxies 63

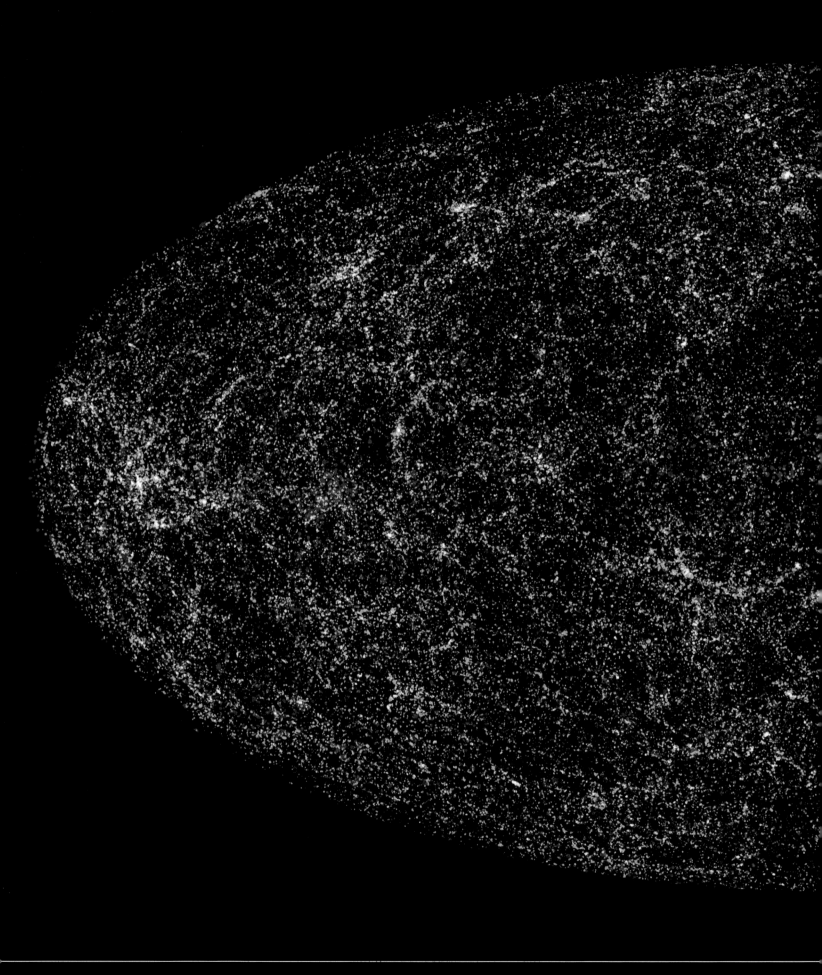

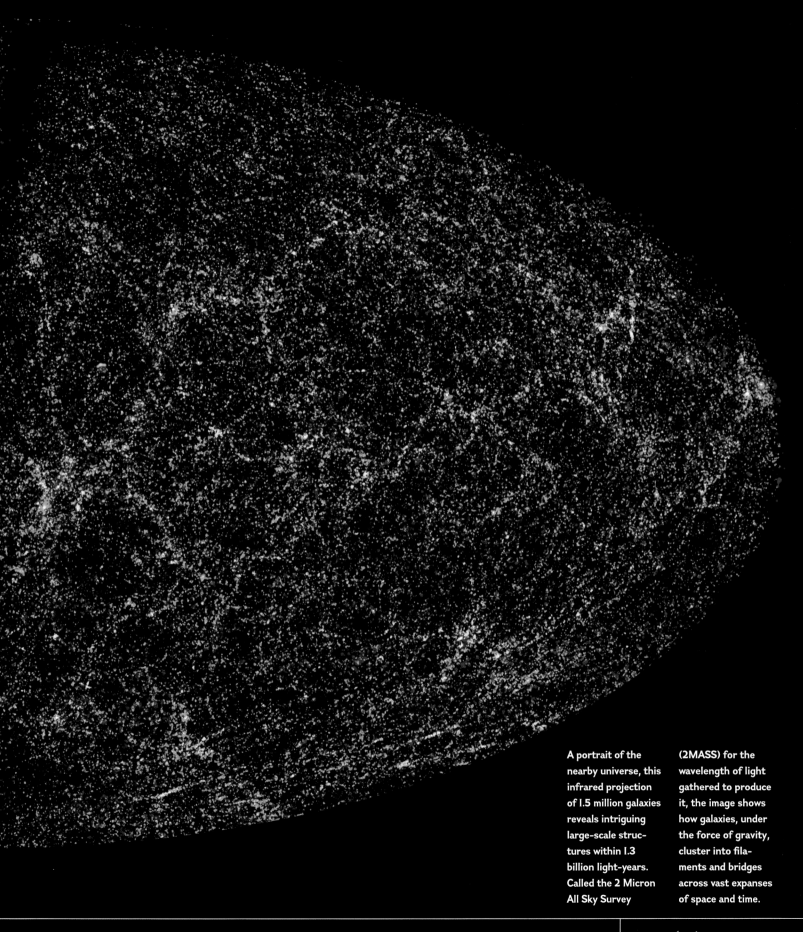

A portrait of the nearby universe, this infrared projection of 1.5 million galaxies reveals intriguing large-scale structures within 1.3 billion light-years. Called the 2 Micron All Sky Survey (2MASS) for the wavelength of light gathered to produce it, the image shows how galaxies, under the force of gravity, cluster into filaments and bridges across vast expanses of space and time.

Honeycombed to save weight, a 6.5-meter telescope mirror under construction at the University of Arizona's Steward Observatory Mirror Laboratory is inspected by a lab manager (left) in 1993.

Aimed due south over the Anglo-Australian Telescope in New South Wales, a time-lapse photo of star trails captures our planet's rotation on its axis.

TELESCOPE TRIVIA

1. Biggest: Keck I and II, Mauna Kea, Hawaii, optical telescopes, each with a ten-meter mirror
2. Highest: Cosmic Background Imager, Llano de Chajnantor, Chile, 16,700 feet
3. Farthest out: SOHO (Solar and Heliospheric Observatory), one million miles from Earth
4. Most stretched out: Very Long Baseline Array, ten radio telescopes spanning 5,860 miles from Hawaii to the Virgin Islands.

ABOVE: ROGER H. RESSMEYER • RIGHT: DAVID MALIN, ANGLO-AUSTRALIAN OBSERVATORY

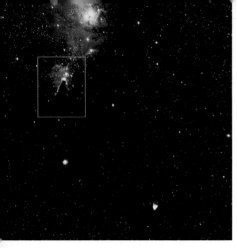

Unveiling distant beauties

Gathering in 1921, scientists and staff at Yerkes Observatory in Wisconsin posed next to the largest refracting telescope ever built (below). Among the scientists, not even visitor Albert Einstein, fifth from right in front row, could have imagined the images to come from future instruments like the Hubble Space Telescope or the wonders they reveal: planets around other stars, black holes at the cores of galaxies, the spectacular birth and death of stars. Peering 2,500 light-years into space, Hubble's Advanced Camera for Surveys captured this view of the Cone Nebula (right), showing three bright newborn stars within a dark cloud of gas and dust, surrounded by a red halo of glowing hydrogen. A February 1949 image of the nebula (top left, in rectangle) made with the Schmidt telescope at Palomar Observatory in California gave few indications of the nebula's dramatic structure.

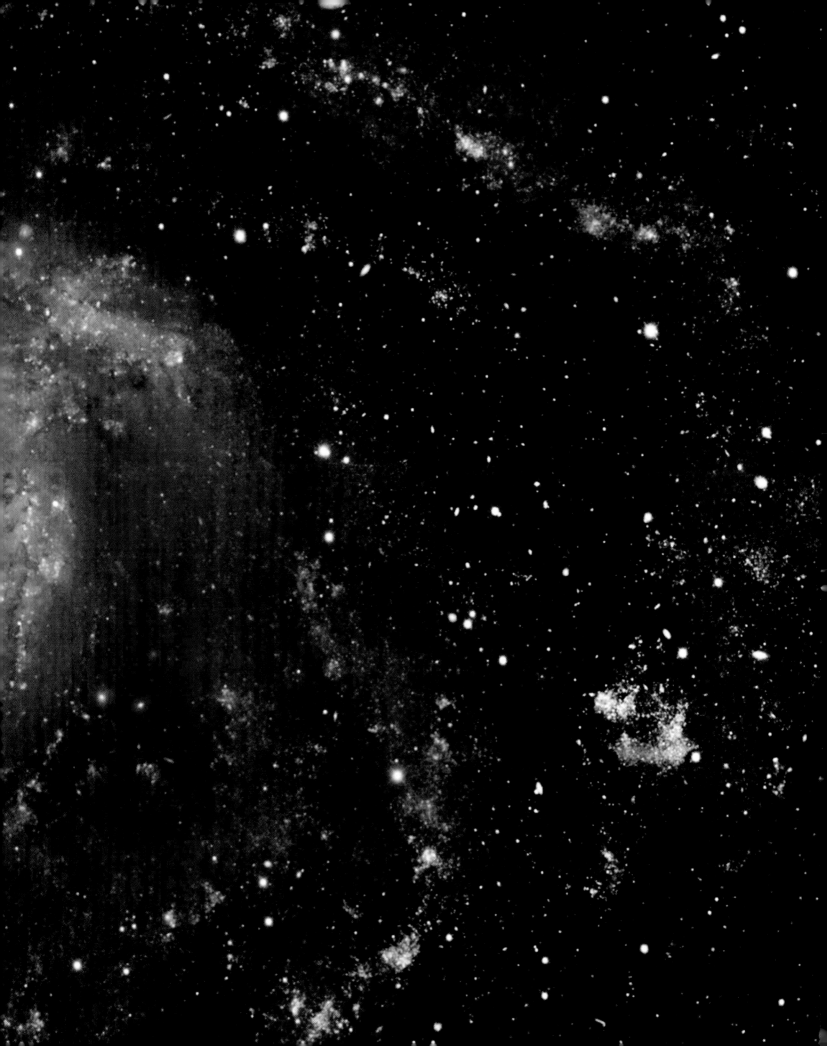

Three views of the Milky Way: An infrared panorama (top), looking toward the core, reveals many billions of stars unobscured by interstellar dust, while a visible light view (middle) shows a band of sky where dust clouds block starlight. An image from NASA's orbiting x-ray observatory, Chandra, focuses on the galaxy's core (bottom), where black holes, white dwarfs, and neutron stars flourish.

Preceding pages: An enchanting spiral galaxy known as Messier 101, or the Pinwheel galaxy, may have had a gravitational brush with another galaxy during the past 100 million years. If so, that would explain its distorted spiral arms, in which young hot stars appear blue and ionized hydrogen sparkles pink.

TOP: JOHN CARPENTER, THOMAS H. JARRETT, AND ROBERT HURT, CALTECH AND 2MASS
CENTER: JOHN GLEASON, CELESTIAL IMAGES • BOTTOM: DANIEL WANG, UNIVERSITY OF

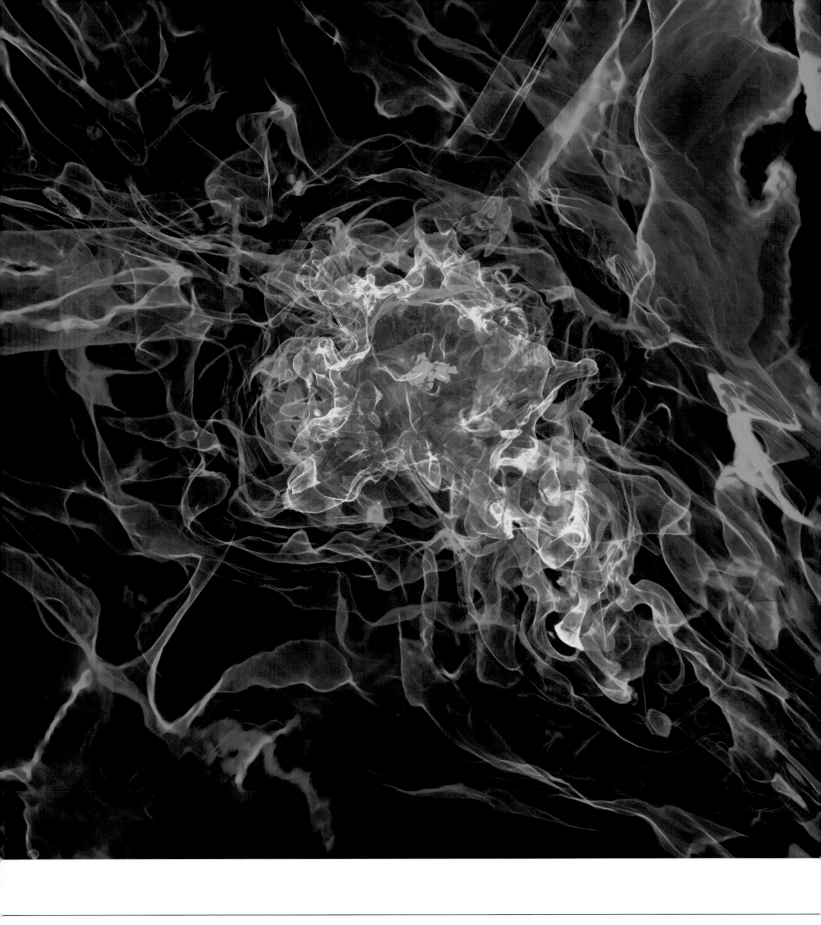

■ See animations of the birth and death of stars, then download a desktop image (opposite, top right) at nationalgeographic.com/magazine/space.

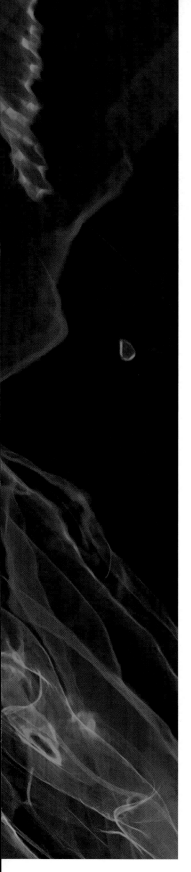

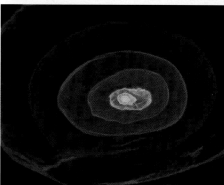

Then there was light

About 100 million to 300 million years after the big bang, in what had been an ocean of darkness, the first star was born. It happened inside a swirling cloud of hydrogen and helium gas gathered together by the gravity of dense, invisible "dark matter," as depicted in a computer simulation (left). As the gases cooled, the center of the cloud collapsed into a dense clump (top right). Zooming deeper into the clump (second and third from top), the simulation reveals a protostar. Over hundreds of thousands of years the clump in turn collapsed, triggering fusion—and a star was born. After a few million years, its fuel exhausted, the star exploded in a supernova (bottom right), seeding the universe with heavy elements such as oxygen and carbon. These new elements would later allow other stars, planets, galaxies—even life itself—to come into existence.

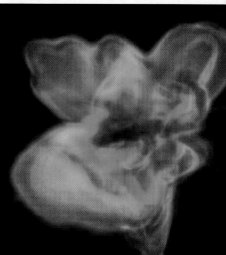

LEFT: RALF KÄHLER, ZUSE INSTITUTE BERLIN/MAX PLANCK INSTITUTE FOR GRAVITATIONAL PHYSICS, AND TOM ABEL, PENNSYLVANIA STATE UNIVERSITY • RIGHT: RALF KÄHLER AND TOM ABEL

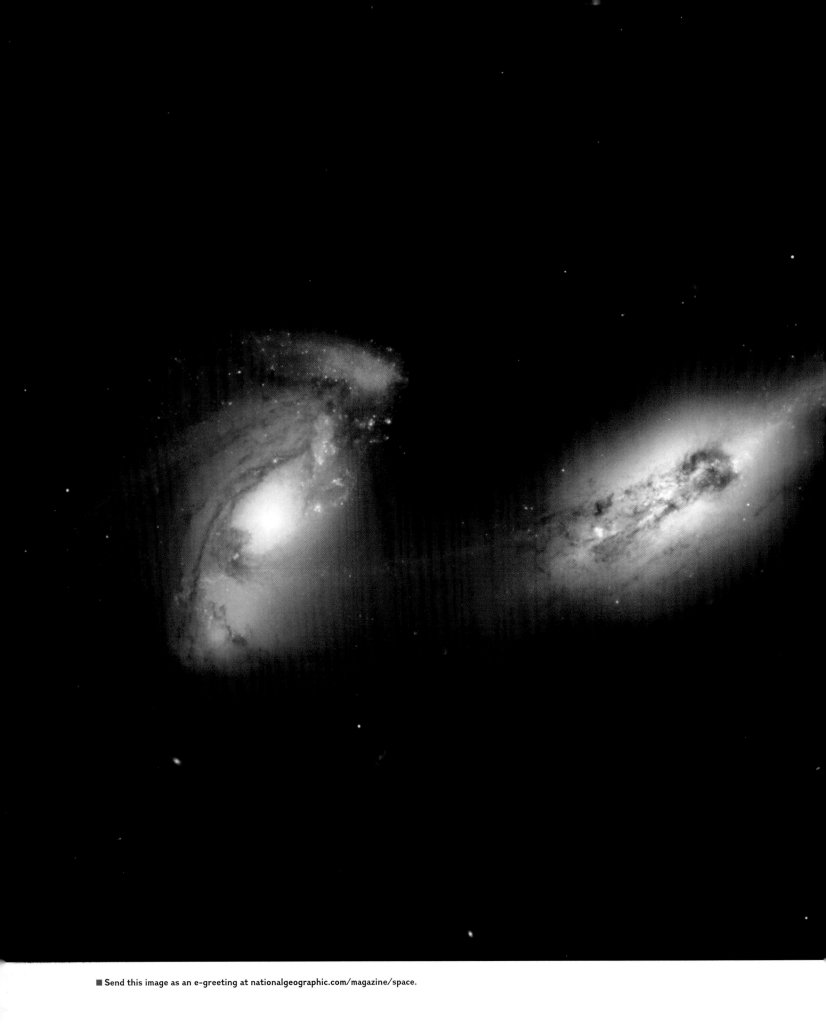

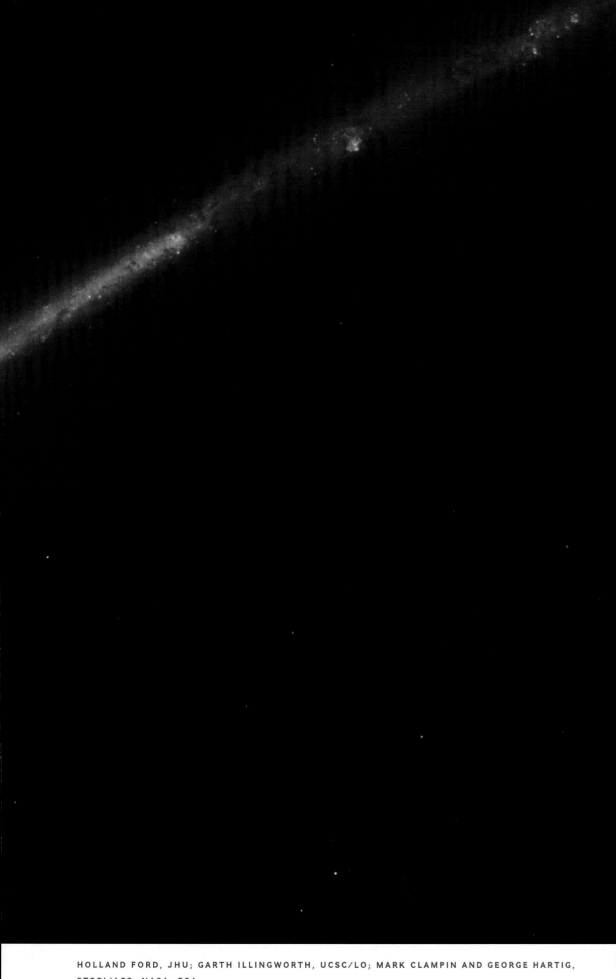

Two galaxies nick-named "the mice" are merging into a huge new one 300 million light-years from Earth. When the galaxies side-swiped each other long ago, they un-raveled long tails of stars and gas.

HOLLAND FORD, JHU; GARTH ILLINGWORTH, UCSC/LO; MARK CLAMPIN AND GEORGE HARTIG, STSCI/ACS; NASA; ESA

It's the stuff of stars, gossamer tangles of gas and dust that linger from a supernova in the Large Magellanic Cloud (left), a nearby companion galaxy to the Milky Way. Over time the material will be recycled into new stars.

Such newborns announce their presence by the scarlet glow of hydrogen, visible around another star-forming region called IC 1396 (right), 2,500 light-years from Earth.

LEFT: YOU-HUA CHU, UNIVERSITY OF ILLINOIS AT URBANA-CHAMPAIGN; SHRI KULKARNI, CALTECH; RICHARD ROTHSCHILD, UNIVERSITY OF CALIFORNIA, SAN DIEGO; NASA/STSCI
ABOVE: JEAN-CHARLES CUILLANDRE, CFHT

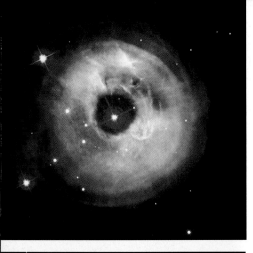

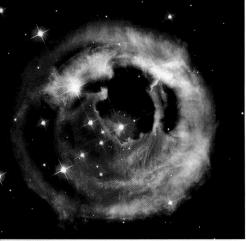

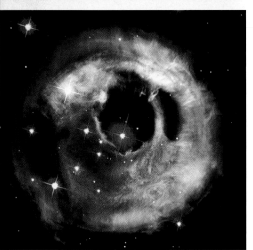

A sudden flash in the dark

In January 2002 a star called V838 Monocerotis, until then an unremarkable pinpoint 20,000 light-years away, suddenly became 600,000 times brighter than our sun. It also swelled to a size that, in our solar system, would have engulfed the orbit of Jupiter. After astronomers reported the star's brightening, operators turned the Hubble Space Telescope toward it and made a series of exposures in 2002 (from top left) on May 20, September 2, October 28, and December 17 (right). Like a flash of lightning behind earthly clouds, the star's light illuminated vast realms of surrounding dust that it may have ejected in previous outbursts. As its waves of light crashed against more distant shoals of debris, a "light echo" formed that should be visible for the rest of this decade.

HOWARD E. BOND AND NASA/STSCI (ALL) • FOLLOWING PAGES: HUBBLE HERITAGE TEAM, NASA/STSCI ■ Send this image as an e-greeting at nationalgeographic.com/magazine/space.

Hats off to Hubble's
spectacular image
of M104, the Som-
brero galaxy, 28
million light-years
from Earth. One of
the most massive
objects in the dense
Virgo cluster of
galaxies, the Som-
brero's bright core
contains a black
hole a billion times
the mass of our sun.

planetary siblings

LIKE ANY BIG FAMILY our solar system can sometimes resemble a collection of oddballs. Four small, rocky planets cling close to mother sun's skirts, while four other siblings, giant balls of gas, don't look like the little ones at all. Tiny Mercury sports a black eye—an 832-mile-wide crater. Smoldering Venus and frigid Mars bookend the favorite, Earth, which enjoys a privileged position where living things thrive. Flamboyant Saturn, it turns out, isn't the only super-size orb wearing a necklace; Jupiter, Uranus, and Neptune have rings too. And the roster of Jupiter's extended family keeps growing— 61 moons at last count, including Io (left), appearing to hover just above the Jovian cloud tops in this image (but in fact keeping its distance 217,500 miles away). Then there's Pluto, a chunk of rock and ice that isn't like any of the others. Following an eccentric orbit tilted away from the rest, Pluto and its moon, Charon, apparently were adopted from the solar suburbs. And we can't forget those party-crashing cousins—comets and asteroids—that sometimes show up unannounced.

■ Available as a desktop image at nationalgeographic.com/magazine/space.

Hidden by Venus's perpetually cloudy atmosphere, volcanoes Sif Mons (right, at left) and Gula Mons rise from a lava plain in this perspective view based on radar data.

Despite surface temperatures of about 880°F, the Soviet lander Venera 9 snapped this picture (bottom) on October 22, 1975, during the 53 minutes it was functional.

Following pages:
Dust storms sweep across the northern plains of Mars in spring, when warm and cold air masses clash, creating stormy weather near the polar ice cap.

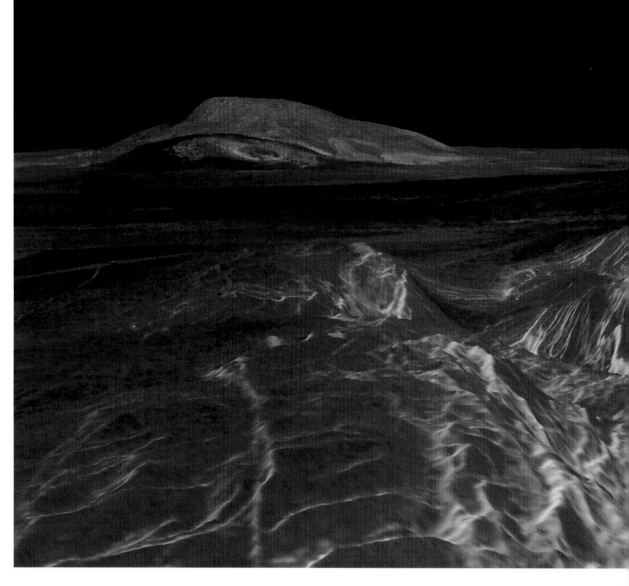

TOP: DAVID P. ANDERSON, SOUTHERN METHODIST UNIVERSITY; NASA/JPL • ABOVE: DON P. MITCHELL • FOLLOWING PAGES: MALIN SPACE SCIENCE SYSTEMS (MSSS); NASA/JPL

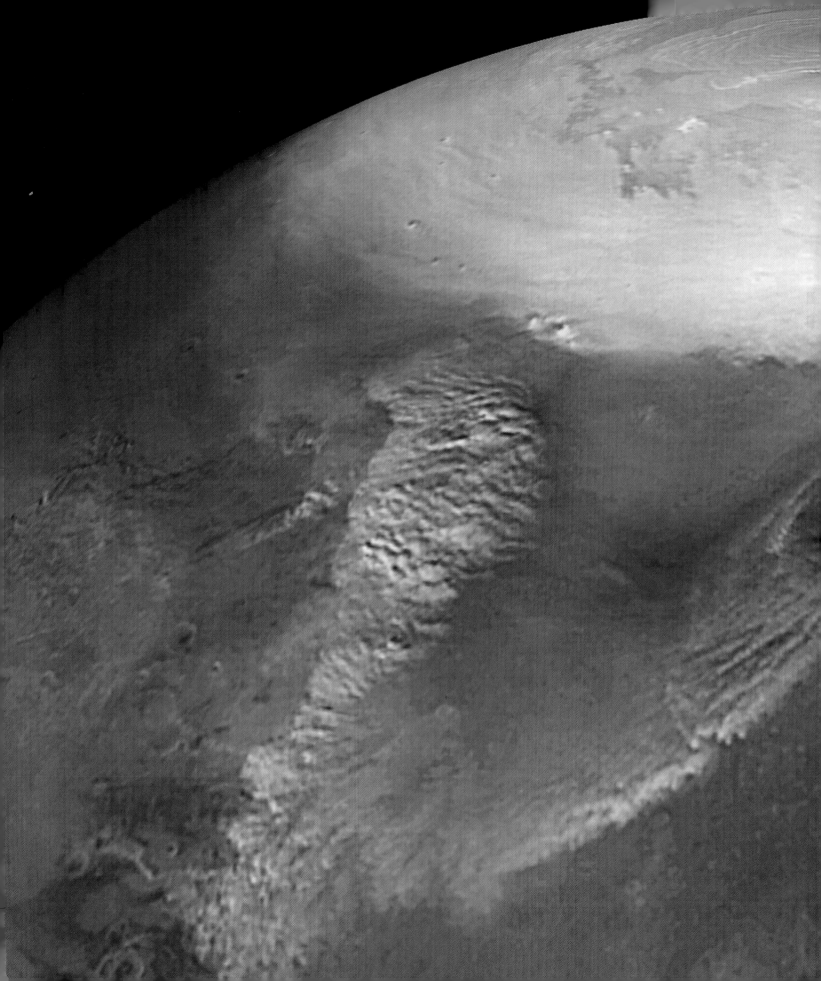

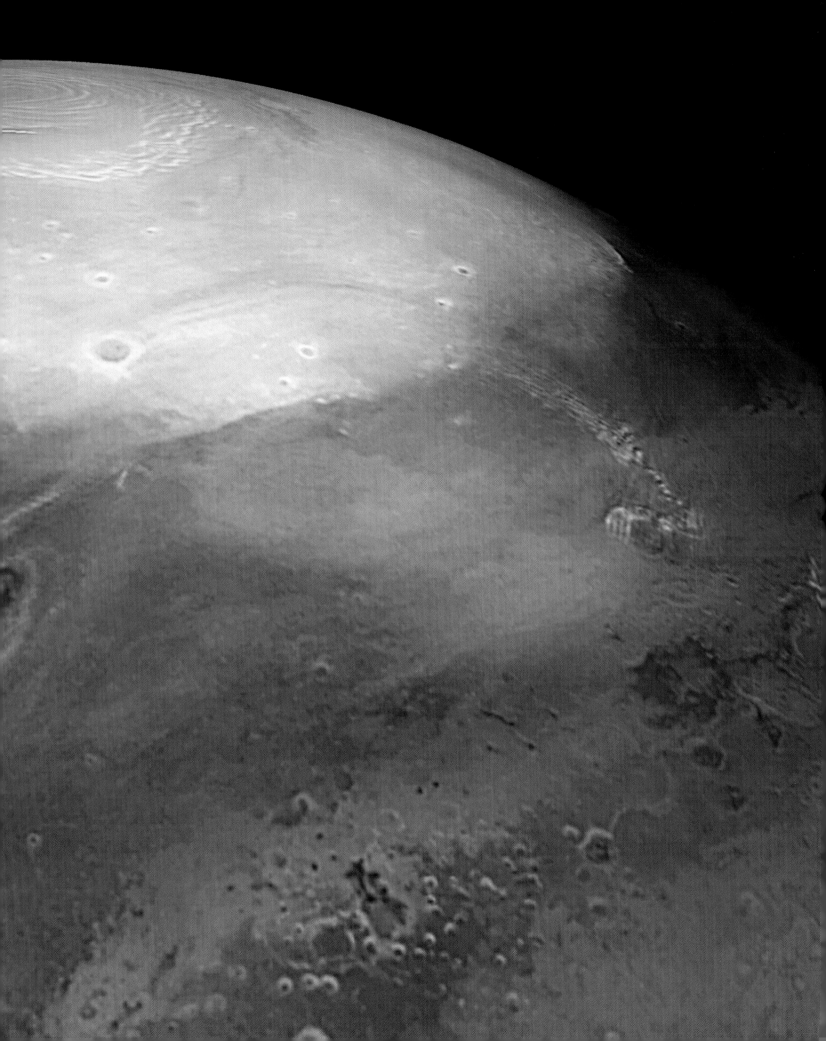

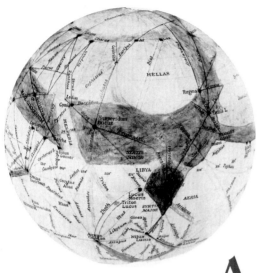

A century of Martian speculation

Peering through his telescope at the turn of the 20th century, Percival Lowell, a wealthy amateur astronomer, was convinced that he'd found signs of intelligent life on Mars. Long delicate lines on the planet's surface, he proposed, were strips of vegetation bordering water-filled canals fed by melting polar ice caps. These canals, depicted on a globe (top) and described in his 1906 book, *Mars and Its Canals,* were dug by beings struggling to survive on a dying world, he theorized. Dark blotches on the planet's surface, visible in a 1907 image (far left) from the Lowell Observatory in Flagstaff, Arizona, were likely vegetation, he wrote. Attempting to verify Lowell's theory, astronomer E. C. Slipher took a color photograph of Mars (near left) in 1954 from South Africa using a 27-inch refracting telescope. The dark areas, he wrote in NATIONAL GEOGRAPHIC, "bear eloquent testimony to the fact that Mars is not a dead world." But when Mariner 9, the first spacecraft to orbit Mars, arrived in 1971, it discovered a very different place—a desert planet of volcanoes, canyons, and dust storms. A portrait taken by the Hubble Space Telescope on August 26, 2003 (right), reveals in sharp detail the darkened areas now known to be crater-pocked wastelands.

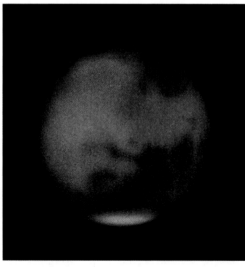

TOP AND BOTTOM LEFT: PERCIVAL LOWELL, LOWELL OBSERVATORY ARCHIVES • BOTTOM RIGHT: E. C. SLIPHER, LOWELL OBSERVATORY ARCHIVES • OPPOSITE: JAMES BELL, CORNELL UNIVERSITY; MICHAEL WOLFF, SPACE SCIENCE INSTITUTE (SSI); NASA/STSCI

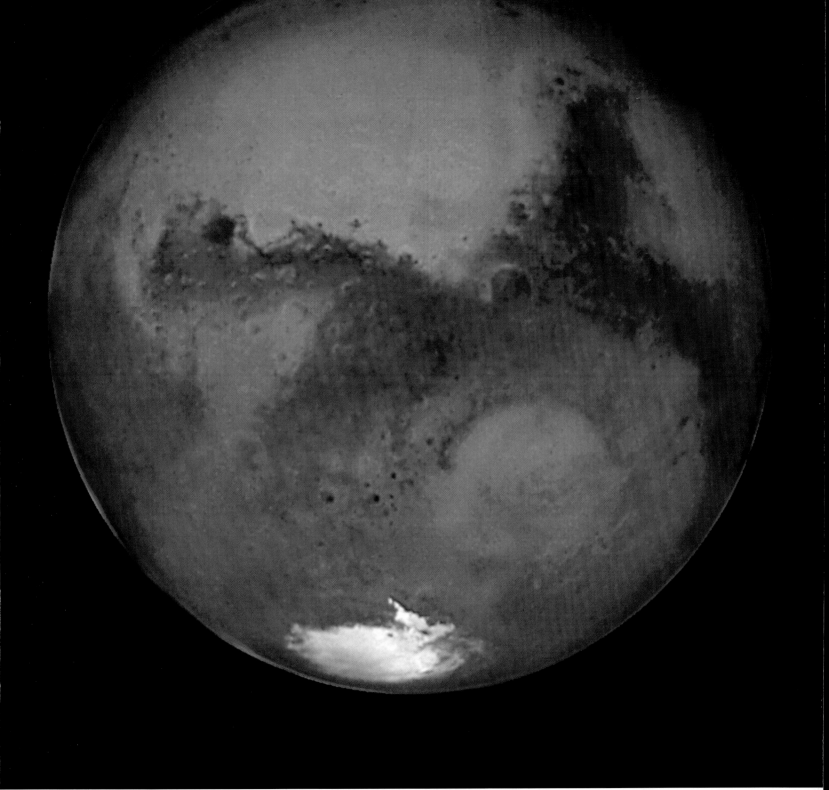

The Viking I lander found Mars to be cold and bleak when it arrived on July 20, 1976, as revealed in this panorama (top). Twenty-one years later, in July 1997, the Mars Pathfinder lander deployed a small rover to explore the rocky terrain, including a bear of a boulder the science team named Yogi.

Find an animation of a Mars landing at

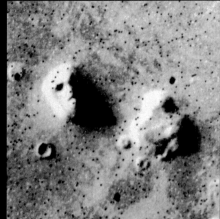

face the facts

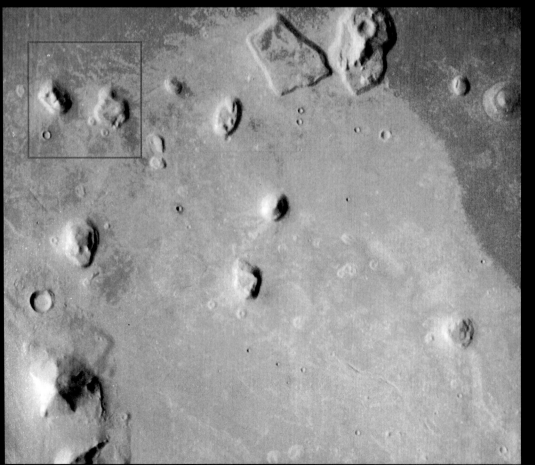

Scanning the surface of Mars in 1976 for a suitable landing spot for the Viking 2 lander, the Viking 1 orbiter photographed the Cydonia region of the northern hemisphere (left) and spotted something intriguing: an object resembling a human face (above). When the picture was released to the public, it set off a flurry of conspiracy theories, including accusations that NASA was withholding evidence that the "face" was not formed naturally. To prove the photo's veracity and to satisfy the public's curiosity, NASA pointed the high-resolution camera aboard the Mars Global Surveyor orbiter toward the mysterious object in April 2001, revealing that the face was nothing more than a large rock formation (right).

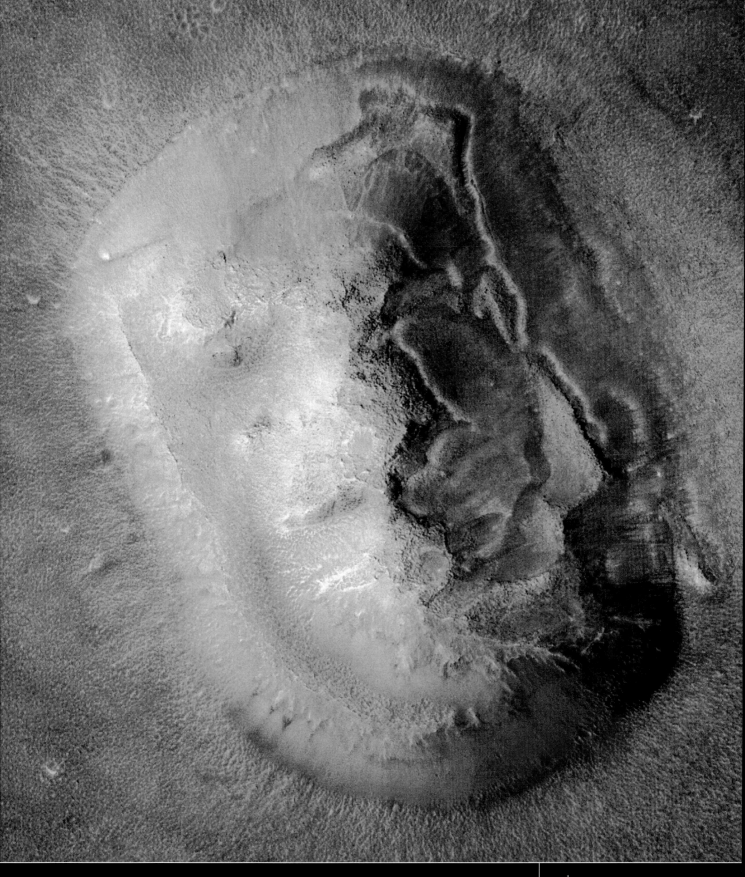

Sculpted by winds, dark sand dunes march across the caldera floor of Nili Patera volcano in the Syrtis Major region of Mars (left). Sedimentary deposits in a crater in the Schiaparelli basin (right) may have been left by the settling of an ancient lake. Confirmation of liquid water in Mars's past or present—imperative for the existence of life as we know it—is a high priority for NASA.

1. Manicouagan crater, Quebec, 60 miles wide, created 210
million years ago by an object perhaps four miles in diameter
2. Chicxulub crater, Yucatán Peninsula, 110 miles wide, 65 million
years ago, six-mile-diameter object
3. Meteor Crater, Arizona, 0.75 miles wide, 49,000 years ago,
object 150-300 feet in diameter
4. Tunguska, Siberia, meteorite exploded before impact, leveling
850 square miles of forest in 1908
5. Near miss: 2002 MN, a 200-foot-diameter asteroid, came
within 74,000 miles of Earth on June 14, 2002
6. Heads up: 1999 AN10, a 2,000-foot-diameter asteroid,
predicted to come within 250,000 miles on August 7, 2027

A relic from the infancy of the solar system, the asteroid Eros (left) was photographed by the NEAR Shoemaker probe after it entered orbit of Eros on Valentine's Day 2000. A year later the spacecraft landed in the saddle-shaped crater of the 21-mile-long rock.

Another survivor from the early solar system, comet Hale-Bopp (right) created a worldwide sensation in 1997. The comet's dirty snowball of a nucleus left bright trails of ionized gas (blue) and dust (white) that stretched for millions of miles.

Jupiter takes a cosmic punch

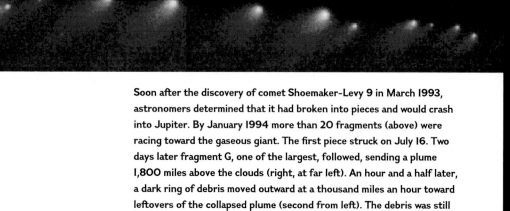

Soon after the discovery of comet Shoemaker-Levy 9 in March 1993, astronomers determined that it had broken into pieces and would crash into Jupiter. By January 1994 more than 20 fragments (above) were racing toward the gaseous giant. The first piece struck on July 16. Two days later fragment G, one of the largest, followed, sending a plume 1,800 miles above the clouds (right, at far left). An hour and a half later, a dark ring of debris moved outward at a thousand miles an hour toward leftovers of the collapsed plume (second from left). The debris was still visible three days later next to new material from fragment L (third from left). Five days after impact (far right) the scars remained, distorted by winds. It was humanity's first view of a collision like the one that helped kill off Earth's dinosaurs 65 million years ago.

ABOVE: HAROLD A. WEAVER, JHU; T. ED SMITH, STSCI; NASA • RIGHT: ROBIN EVANS AND JOHN T. TRAUGER, JPL; HEIDI HAMMEL, SSI; HUBBLE SPACE TELESCOPE COMET SCIENCE TEAM/NASA/STSCI ■ E-greet a friend (right) at nationalgeographic.com/magazine/space.

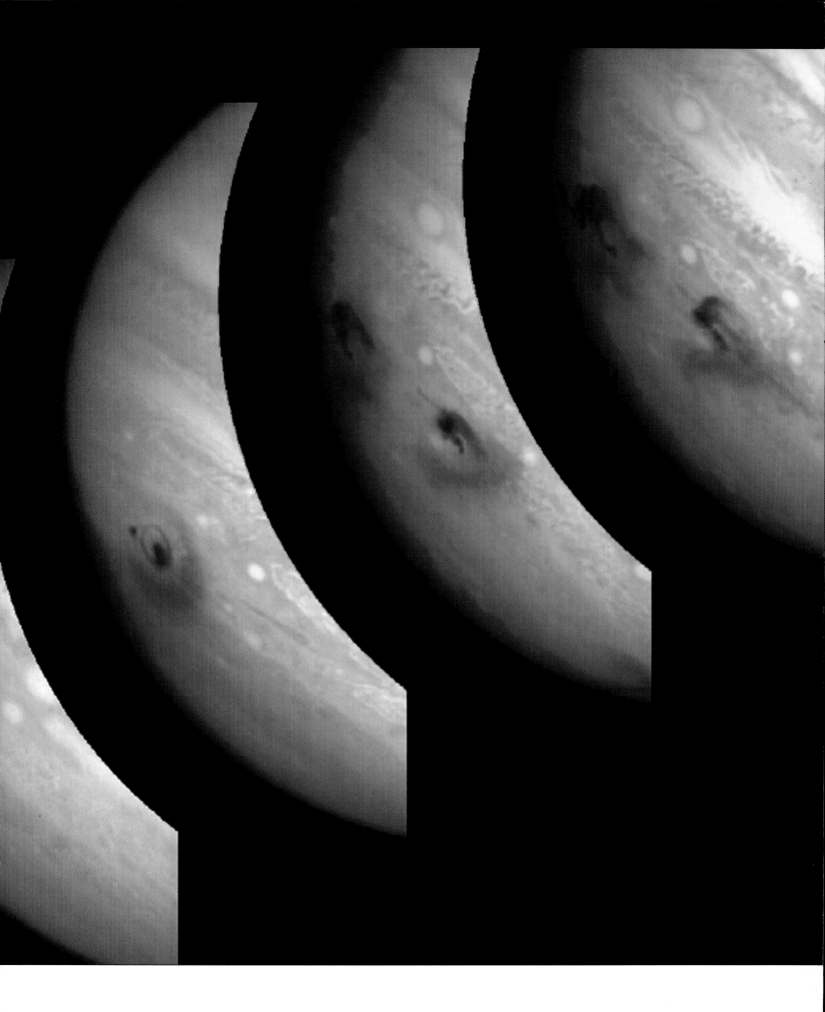

Pockmarked Callisto, giant Ganymede, fractured Europa, and volcanic Io (left, top to bottom) make up this family album of Jupiter's largest moons. A closer look at Europa (right) reveals a chaotic crust of ice, perhaps ten miles thick, that appears to have been broken into shifting rafts by heat from below. Evidence suggests that a vast ocean of liquid water lies beneath Europa's surface, potentially creating favorable conditions for life.

Galileo called them "ears" when he first observed Saturn's rings almost four centuries ago. In 1981 NASA's Voyager 2 spacecraft revealed mysterious dark spokes (left) in the multibanded rings of dust and ice.

Glowing like fluorescent wildfires, auroral curtains appear at both of Saturn's poles (right) in an ultraviolet image from the Hubble Space Telescope.

MOST DISTANT SPACE PROBES

1. Voyager 1, now 8.5 billion miles from Earth, launched 1977, Jupiter and Saturn flybys
2. Pioneer 10, 7.8 billion miles, 1972, Jupiter
3. Voyager 2, 6.8 billion miles, 1977, Jupiter, Saturn, Uranus, Neptune
4. Pioneer 11, 6 billion miles, 1973, Jupiter and Saturn
5. Cassini-Huygens, 743 million miles, 1997, Saturn orbiter and Titan probe

> "It came as a great shock to me, in childhood days, to learn that our sun was something called a 'yellow dwarf' and that sophisticated people scorned it as an insignificant member of the Milky Way." —ISAAC ASIMOV

Plasma dances madly within the sun's corona, its outermost atmosphere, in an x-ray image (right) from the Japanese-launched Yohkoh satellite, whose name means "sunbeam." Some 42 million miles away from the surface, Mercury marches across the sun's face (below) during a rarely seen transit in 2003.

Following pages: Earth-size sunspots mark strong magnetic fields that block heat gushing from the sun's core, creating cooler areas that are still a mystery to experts.

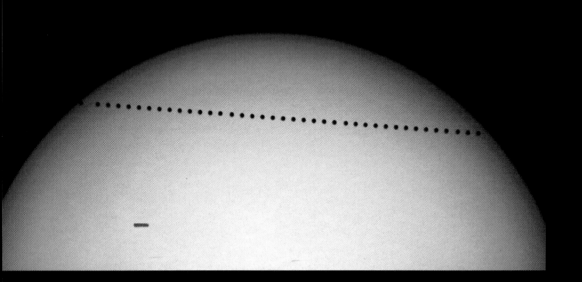

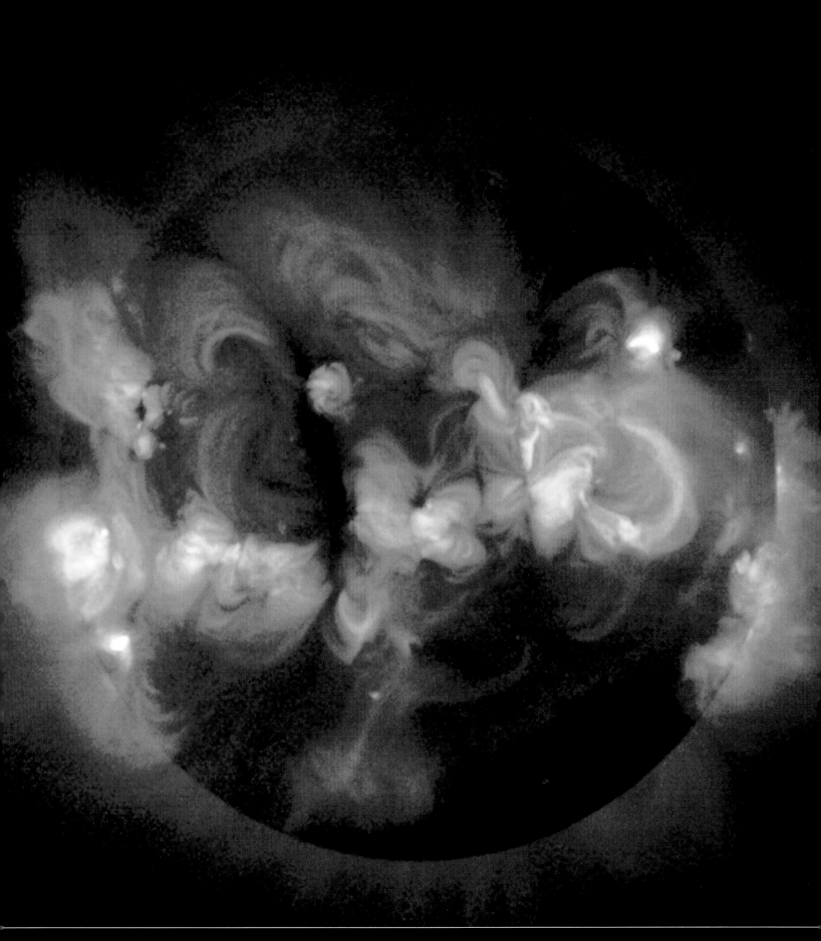

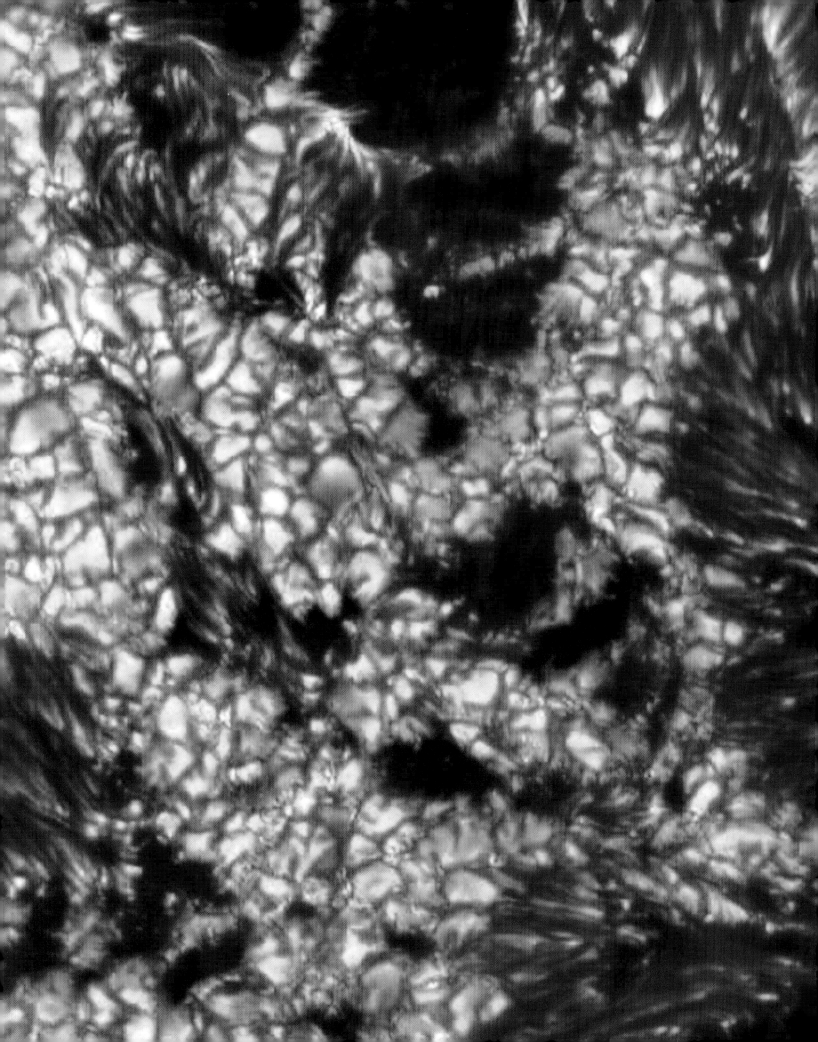

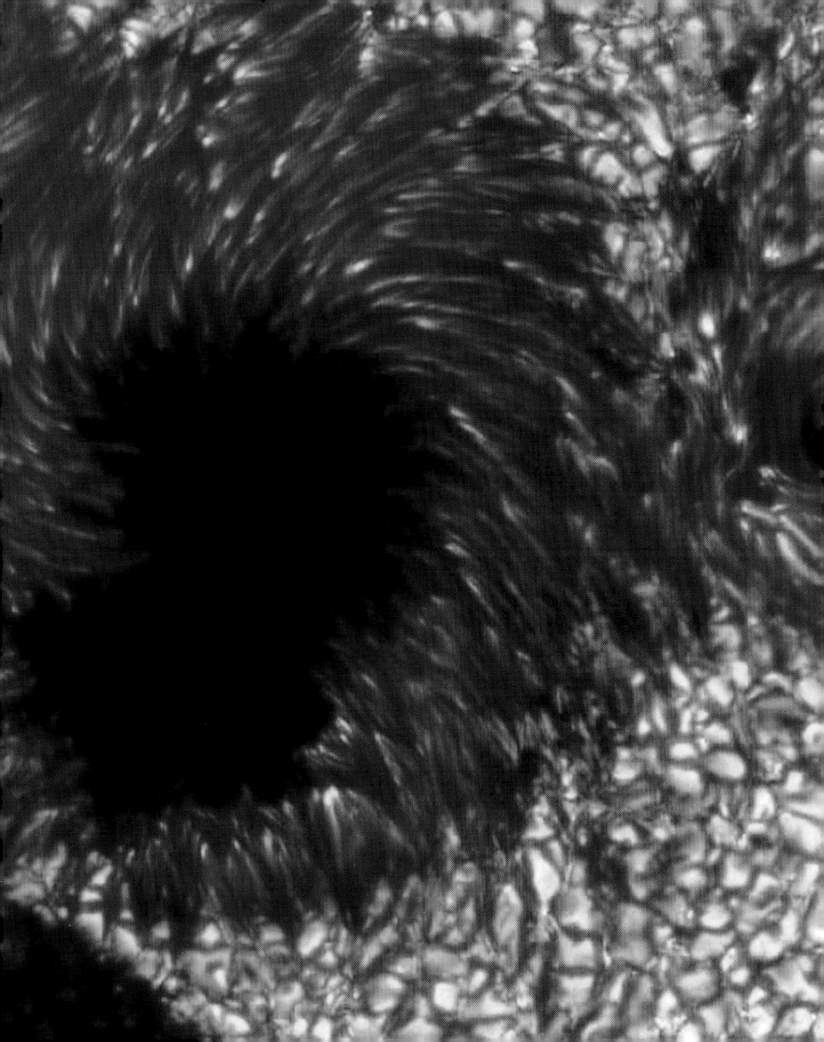

a world called home

NO MATTER HOW MANY TIMES astronauts have photographed it during two decades of space shuttle missions, the image in the rearview mirror has never become routine: that perfect blue marble, whorled with white, suspended against blackest space.

Looking down on the Pacific in September 1984, the crew of *Discovery* saw the volcano Pagan, at far left, belching brown ash into the sky over the Northern Mariana Islands, and fields of clouds pilling into fluffy white balls of lint. Such views not only inspire us but also remind us of the volatile forces—water, wind, fire—that formed and still sculpt the land. And though our failings are visible too— the scars of deforestation, pollution, and the smoke of battle between nations—political borders become irrelevant: From orbit the planet is revealed to be a single entity, a shared home. Surely visitors from another world, no matter what marvels they may have seen en route, would be awed by the glory of Earth.

■ Available as a desktop image at nationalgeographic.com/magazine/space.

The southern lights flicker over a cloud-covered Indian Ocean in this shot from the space shuttle *Discovery.* Like auroras on other planets, these dancing curtains of color normally occur near the poles, where Earth's magnetic field allows charged particles from the sun to strike oxygen atoms and nitrogen molecules in the upper atmosphere.

Following pages: Bright lights reveal big cities in western Europe, Japan, and the eastern U.S. in this composite image of the planet at night from military weather satellites. Other less urbanized places, such as western China and most of Africa, remain dark.

ABOVE: NASA PHOTOGRAPH DIGITIZED BY CORBIS CORPORATION © 1996

■ Learn more about how auroras work and see them in motion at nationalgeographic.com/magazine/space.

A planet of ever shifting shapes

Winds sweeping across the sands of eastern Saudi Arabia have carved the Al Kidan dune field (left) into a dramatic pattern of shark's teeth, as seen from the space shuttle *Atlantis* 181 miles up. Other landforms viewed from space —braided rivers, crinkled mountains, slender barrier islands—tell a similar story of change. An earlier crew on *Atlantis* saw the Galápagos Islands (right) as Charles Darwin never could: Lava flows smudge the sparsely vegetated slopes of Isabela and Fernandina, two of the most volcanically active of the islands visited by the naturalist in 1835.

Still evolving as a mountain range, the Himalaya near Mount Everest (at center, following pages) may be growing in height by as much as 0.25 inches a year and drifting northeast by about 1.75 inches a year. Looking down on Everest from the shuttle *Atlantis* in 1994, Scott Parazynski had mixed feelings. The astronaut, who took the photo, had planned to be on an expedition to the mountain that season, but ended up in orbit instead.

■ Rotate a 360-degree view from Everest's summit at nationalgeographic.com/magazine/space.

ALSO VISIBLE FROM ORBIT

1. The Pyramids at Giza
2. Houston's intercontinental airport
3. Trans-Siberian Railway
4. Irrigation circles in Kansas
5. Kennedy Space Center
6. Golden Gate Bridge

A bird's-eye view of San Francisco (left) from the Space Imaging Corporation's IKONOS satellite shows downtown buildings in sharp detail from 420 miles up.

Central Baghdad is darkened by trails of smoke from oil fires (right) in this image from NASA's Terra satellite in March 2003. The fires were set along roads and canals by Iraqi forces in an attempt to obscure the capital during the advance of U.S. forces.

ABOVE: SPACE IMAGING • OPPOSITE: UNITED STATES/JAPAN ASTER SCIENCE TEAM; NASA/GSFC; JAPAN MINISTRY OF INTERNATIONAL TRADE AND INDUSTRY; EARTH REMOTE SENSING DATA ANALYSIS CENTER; JAPAN RESOURCES OBSERVATION SYSTEM ORGANIZATION

"Memories of space flight are fleeting. What you have left when you get back are your pictures." —JERRY ROSS, ASTRONAUT

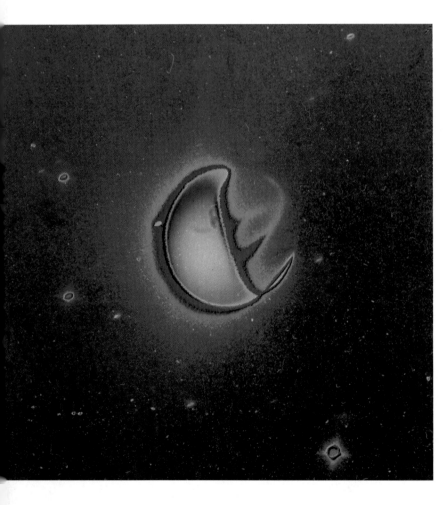

Looking back at Earth from the moon, Apollo 16 astronauts took this color-enhanced ultraviolet portrait (left), which shows oxygen density in the atmosphere on the daylight side.

Twisted into a spiral of 100-mile-an-hour winds, Hurricane Isabel (right) aims for the North Carolina coast, where it made landfall on September 18, 2003.

Following pages: Clouds blanket the Pacific Ocean as a full moon sets in this peaceful view from the space shuttle *Columbia.*

ABOVE: NASA • RIGHT: ORBIMAGE • FOLLOWING PAGES: NASA PHOTO-GRAPH DIGITIZED BY CORBIS CORPORATION © 1996 ■ Step into the eye of Hurricane Isabel, then e-greet a friend at nationalgeographic.com/magazine/space.

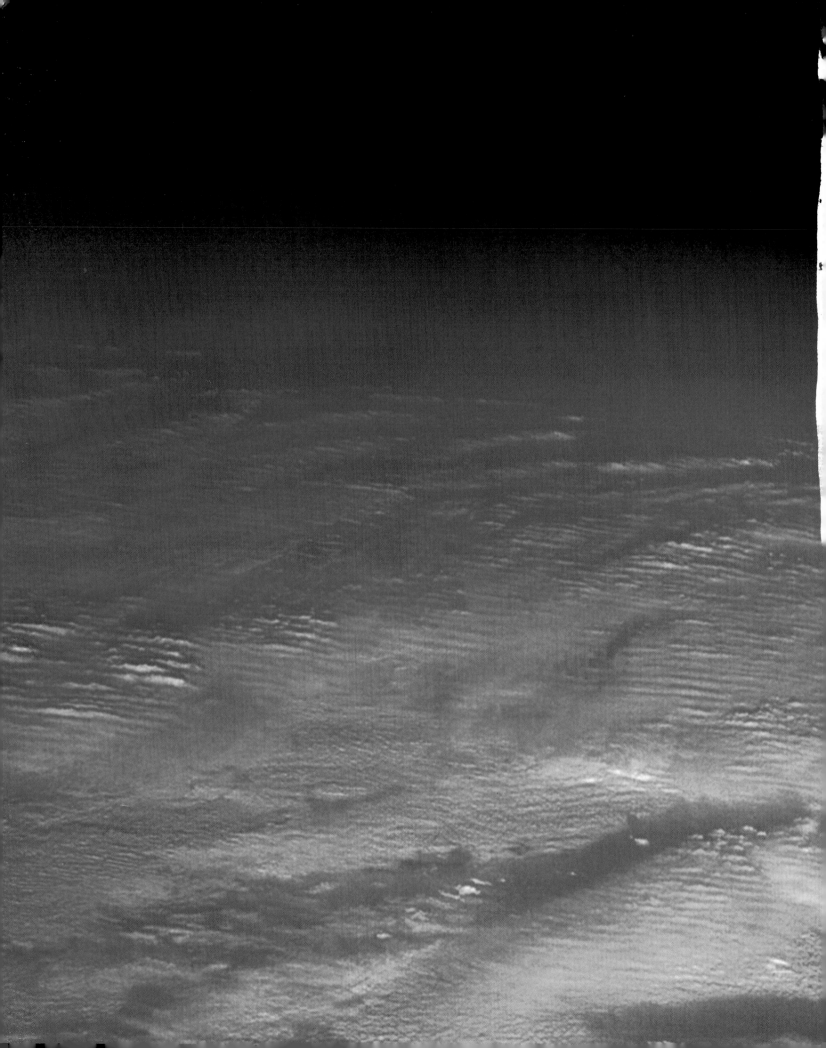

what a ride

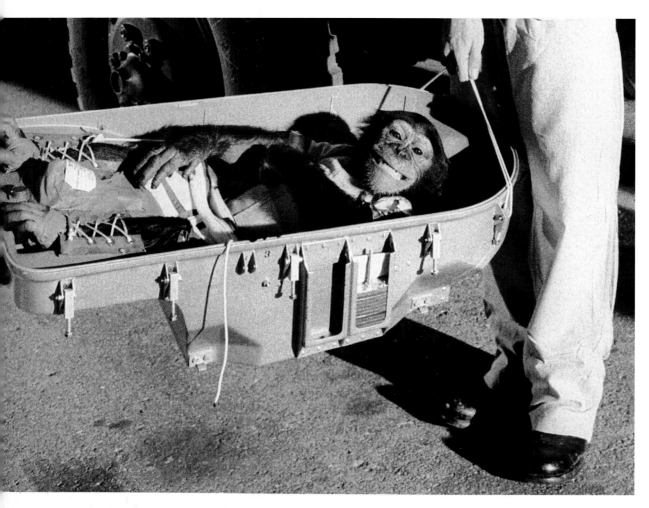

Getting a hero's welcome, NASA's "chimponaut" Ham is presented to the press on January 31, 1961. Three months before the first U.S. astronaut would blast off, the chimpanzee had been strapped into a pressurized couch, locked into the Mercury capsule, and shot into the sky on a 16-minute 39-second flight. Pronounced healthy after splashing down in the Atlantic, Ham was given an early retirement and later spent most of his days at the National Zoo in Washington, D.C. His legacy had been established as a true explorer, one of the first pioneers on the final frontier.

RALPH CRANE, *LIFE* ■ Test your knowledge of our cosmos at nationalgeographic.com/magazine/space.